Sing!
a new creation

Calvin Institute of Christian Worship
Grand Rapids, Michigan

CRC Publications
Grand Rapids, Michigan

Reformed Church Press
New York, New York

Sing! A New Creation
Pew Edition

Other editions:
Leader's Edition
Software Edition

Sing! A New Creation is copublished by

The Calvin Institute of Christian Worship, 3201 Burton SE, Grand Rapids, MI 49546; Phone: (616) 957-6088; Fax: (616) 957-8454; E-mail: worship@calvin.edu; Web site: www.calvin.edu/worship.

Faith Alive Christian Resources, a ministry of CRC Publications, 2850 Kalamazoo Ave. SE, Grand Rapids, MI 49560; Phone: (800) 333-8300; E-mail: info@faithaliveresources.org; Web site: www.FaithAliveResources.org.

Reformed Church in America, Office of Worship, RCA Distribution Center, 4500 60th Street SE, Grand Rapids, MI 49512; Phone: (800) 968-7221; Fax: (616) 698-6606; E-mail: orders@rca.org; Web site: www.rca.org.

Printed in the United States of America on recycled paper. ♻

ISBN 1-56212-811-6

10 9 8 7 6 5 4 3 2 1

Design: Dean Heetderks
Copyright administration: Deanne Commeret

Contents

Preface

Sing! A New Creation is a collection of worship songs from the last half of the twentieth century, a period of one of the greatest outpourings of hymns, psalms, and worship songs in all of history. Most songs in the collection were written in the last fifty years. The church of Jesus Christ has been greatly influenced during those fifty years by changes that have resulted in growing diversity in worship practices. On the technological side, churches may have hymnals, but they also have access to copy machines, copyright licenses, and recordings to make new worship songs accessible. On the sociological side, North American congregations, which once reflected their often homogeneous ethnic origins, are reflecting the diversity of communities that are being transformed by mobile populations, an influential youth culture, and individualistic approaches to life.

With so many new songs and growing cultural diversity, congregations have more complex choices to make than ever before. So do hymnal committees. Most congregations use hymnals; many supplement their hymnals with new songs in bulletins or on video projection systems; some have abandoned hymnals altogether. One of the losses when hymnals are no longer used is a common body of songs; in the last generation the number of hymns known by most Christians even within denominations has shrunk dramatically. What is a favorite in one congregation may be unknown to another, often making it difficult for Christians to worship together.

Sing! A New Creation is a declaration that hymnals are important for encouraging Christians to sing songs that connect them to the larger body of Christ. It reveals a conviction that every congregation will be blessed by moving beyond its current repertoire. It is a testimony that the diversity of new worship songs from our various cultures is to be welcomed and embraced as a gift from God. God is calling many different people to live in community, to demonstrate to the world that our unity is found not in style or tradition, but in being members of one body, honoring one Lord, one faith, one baptism, one God of us all (Eph. 4:4-6). Therefore this is no homogeneous collection of songs marketed to one part of the church. *Sing! A New Creation* reflects the rich variety in the church today.

Sing! A New Creation is not intended to stand alone, but rather as a supplement to hymnals that include the rich tradition of Christian hymnody. The Christian Reformed Church (CRC) and the Reformed Church in America (RCA) both produced hymnals in the 1980s; but, while a hymnal used to last a generation, the many new songs and growing diversity of repertoire from one congregation to the next has shortened the shelf life of many hymnals. Thus, the CRC and RCA along with the Calvin Institute of Christian Worship decided to work together in preparing a new hymnal that would reflect the growing landscape of worship music as well as supplement the hymnals used in many churches. A committee of ten—five from the CRC and five from the RCA— met for three years to gather the songs in this collection.

The committee's earliest decisions were to concentrate on the last fifty years and to not repeat anything already available in our denominational hymnals. Our guiding principle was to choose a balance of songs in three different categories.

First, we included new hymns that have the traditional structure of multiple stanzas in metrical form; often, new texts are set to older familiar tunes. Second, we included songs from around the world, often retaining a stanza or two of the original language. Third, we included a wide range of choruses and contemporary songs from the "Praise & Worship" repertoire by such publishers as Maranatha! Music, Integrity, and Vineyard; from the Communities of Taizé in France and Iona in Scotland; and from folk liturgical sources arising out of the Roman Catholic reforms of the Second Vatican Council. In addition, psalms are found throughout the collection in all three categories; some psalm settings are metrical, some come from global sources, and many are found in choruses and other contemporary songs. Also interspersed throughout the collection are spoken prayers and litanies.

From the beginning, the committee was concerned that new styles require new approaches; for example, congregations familiar only with the organ would be encouraged to use other instruments in order to bring particular songs to life. From this concern came the conviction that a Leader's Edition would be not only helpful, but necessary for helping worship leaders and musicians. A generous grant made that hope a reality. This pew edition includes everything the congregation needs. The leader's edition includes all accompaniments, including many parts for different instruments; song notes that give background information and teaching tips for each song; several articles on the different song styles represented; and a large number of indexes.

The structure of the hymnal follows the basic structure of a worship service, beginning with gathering songs and moving all the way to blessing and parting songs. Our prayer is that people who sing from this collection will know the joy of joining their voices with brothers and sisters around the world and in their own congregations—old and young, those who are new to the faith and those who grew up in the church, those who love the old hymns and those who find inspiration in new worship songs. May together we sing praise to the God who is making all things new in Christ.

Sing! A New Creation Committee:
Barbara Boertje
Emily R. Brink
James Hart Brumm
Alfred V. Fedak
John Paarlberg
Bert Polman
Charsie Sawyer
Annetta Vander Lugt
Amy Van Gunst
John D. Witvliet

Acknowledgments

Any hymnal project involves many people, and a particular delight in this project was to work with so many living authors and composers; our thanks to the many who contributed texts and music. We also thank the RCA Worship Commission and the CRC Publications Board for their help in reviewing drafts and overseeing the work of the committee. Several congregations hosted evenings of trying out new songs; committee members benefited greatly from their responses.

Three of the ten committee members named above serve as staff members of the three copublishers: editor Emily R. Brink as worship and music editor for CRC Publications, John Paarlberg as minister for worship and social witness for the Reformed Church in America, and John D. Witvliet as director of the Calvin Institute of Christian Worship. The other seven members contributed their time as volunteers, and special thanks are due them: Barbara Boertje, minister of music at the First Reformed Church, Grandville,

Michigan; text subcommittee chair James Hart Brumm, pastor of Blooming Grove Reformed Church, Defreestville, New York; Alfred V. Fedak, minister of music and the arts at Westminster Presbyterian Church, Albany, New York; committee chair Bert Polman, professor of music at Redeemer University College, Ancaster, Ontario; Charsie Sawyer, professor of voice at Calvin College, Grand Rapids, Michigan; music subcommittee chair Annetta Vander Lugt, music coordinator at Neland Avenue Christian Reformed Church, Grand Rapids, Michigan; and Amy Van Gunst, social worker and pastor in the Reformed Church in America, who served on the RCA Worship Commission. Deanne Commeret, administrative assistant, and Ron Rienstra, associate worship and music editor at CRC Publications, provided invaluable support during the project. Two consultants were particularly helpful on the global songs: C. Michael Hawn and Jorge Lockward. Finally, a generous and significant grant from the ICN Foundation made it possible to publish two editions; without that financial support only one printed edition would have been possible—with fewer songs and without the expanded accompaniments and resources provided in the Leader's Edition.

We acknowledge the goodness of God that has enabled a very diverse committee to work together in harmony throughout this project. May all those who use this hymnal be blessed, as we have been, by singing these songs. May God continue to work in and through us to bring hope and healing to the people of God—indeed, to the whole creation. May we be strengthened as we sing of God's love for us and of our love for God and his growing church gathered in local communities and around the world.

Key to Terms, Symbols, and Abbreviations

alt.	altered
adapt.	adapted by
arr.	arranged by
attr.	attributed to
b.	born
c.	circa (around)
capo	for guitarists, to indicate an alternative key
cent.	century
CM	common meter (86 86)
CMD	common meter double (86 86 86 86)
D.C.	*da capo* (return to beginning)
desc.	descant by
D.S.	*dal segno* (return to sign 𝄋)
harm.	harmonized by
LM	long meter (88 88)
LMD	long meter double (88 88 88 88)
N.C.	no chord (guitar)
para.	paraphrased by
rev.	revised by
SM	short meter (66 86)
st.	stanza(s)
tr.	translated by
vers.	versified by

1 Sing a New Song

Text and music: Daniel L. Schutte (b. 1947)

© 1972, 1974, Daniel L. Schutte, admin. New Dawn Music/OCP Publications

Prayer for the Opening of Worship

God of all glory,
on this first day of the week
you began creation,
bringing light out of darkness.
On this first day
you began your new creation,
raising Jesus Christ out of the darkness of death.

**On this Lord's day
grant that we,
the people you create by water and the Spirit,
may be joined with all your works
in praising you for your great glory.
Through Jesus Christ,
in union with the Holy Spirit,
we praise you now and forever.
Amen.**

Come into God's Presence

3

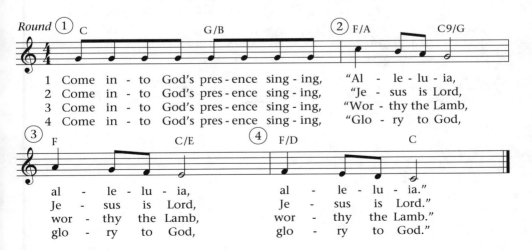

Round ① C   G/B   ② F/A   C9/G

1 Come in - to God's pres - ence sing - ing, "Al - le - lu - ia,
2 Come in - to God's pres - ence sing - ing, "Je - sus is Lord,
3 Come in - to God's pres - ence sing - ing, "Wor - thy the Lamb,
4 Come in - to God's pres - ence sing - ing, "Glo - ry to God,

③ F   C/E   ④ F/D   C

al - le - lu - ia, al - le - lu - ia."
Je - sus is Lord, Je - sus is Lord."
wor - thy the Lamb, wor - thy the Lamb."
glo - ry to God, glo - ry to God."

Text and music: Anonymous

4   Uyai Mose / Come, All You People

Text: St. 1, Alexander Gondo (20th cent., Zimbabwe), tr. I-to Loh (b. 1936); st. 2-3, *With One Voice* (1995)   56 56 56 7
Music: Alexander Gondo; arr. John L. Bell (b. 1949)   UYAI MOSE

Jesu, tawa pano / Jesus, We Are Here

Other stanzas may be added:
Father, we are here . . .
Spirit, we are here . . .

Text and music: Patrick Matsikenyiri (20th cent., Zimbabwe); Sp. tr. Pedro P. Pirón (b. 20th cent.);
desc. Jorge Lockward (b. 1965)

6   Come and Let Us Worship God

1 Come and let us wor-ship God,
2 Though our cul-ture goes a - stray,
3 Let us hear our Mak-er's voice,

1 Come and wor-ship
2 Cul - ture goes a -
3 Hear our Mak-er's

turn to serve the liv - ing Lord,
keen to find an ea - sier way,
and let Christ in - form each choice.

God,
stray,
voice,

serve the liv - ing
keen to find a
Christ in - form each

move from where we are mis - led,
let our eyes be on God's care
Sis - ter, bro-ther, wo-men, men:

Lord,
way,
choice.

are mis - led,
on God's care
All to - geth - er

Text and music: Cranmer Muhabura (20th cent.); tr. and arr. John Bell (b. 1949)

Tr. and arr. © 1997, WGRG the Iona Community (Scotland), admin. GIA Publications, Inc.

do   as   an - cient pro - phets   said.
ev - i - dent and ev - ery - where.
let   us   turn   to   God   a - gain.

Refrain

Oh, our ev - er lov - ing   God,   we, the crea - tures

of your Word,   come to make our home in   you,

know - ing that your Word is   true.

7 Psalm 122: I Rejoiced When I Heard Them Say

I re-joiced when I heard them say, "Let us go to the house of the Lord." And now our feet are stand-ing with-in your gates, Je-ru-sa-lem. lem. 1,4 Je-

(4) ru-sa-lem, God's ci-ty, built strong by the hand of the Lord. To Je-ru-sa-lem will the tribes go up, the peo-ple of our God.

2 For the peace of Je-ru-sa-lem we pray; may peace come to your homes. For the love of my rel-a-tives and friends, may peace come to you.

3 For the love of the house of the Lord, I will pray for you. May the throne of jus-tice be re-stored in you. 4 Je

Text and music: Psalm 122; vers. John Michael Talbot (b. 1954)

Gather Us In

1 Here in this place— new light is stream-ing, now is the dark - ness
2 We are the young, our lives are a mys - tery, we are the old who
3 Here we will take the wine and the wa - ter, here we will take the
4 Not in the dark of build-ings con-fin - ing, not in some heav - en,

van-ished a - way; see in this space our fears and our dream-ings
yearn for your face; we have been sung through-out all of his - tory,
bread of new birth, here you shall call your sons and your daugh-ters,
light years a - way— here in this place the new light is shin - ing,

brought here to you in the light of this day.
called to be light to the whole hu - man race.
call us a - new to be salt for the earth.
now is the king-dom, and now is the day.

Gath-er us in, the lost and for - sak - en, gath-er us in, the
Gath-er us in, the rich and the haugh-ty, gath-er us in, the
Give us to drink the wine of com - pas - sion, give us to eat the
Gath-er us in and hold us for - ev - er, gath-er us in and

blind and the lame; call to us now, and we shall a - wak - en,
proud and the strong; give us a heart, so meek and so low - ly,
bread that is you; nour-ish us well, and teach us to fash-ion
make us your own; gath - er us in, all peop-les to-geth - er,

we shall a - rise at the sound of our name.
give us the cour-age to en - ter the song.
lives that are ho - ly and hearts that are true.
fire— of love in our flesh and our bone.

Text and music: Marty Haugen (b. 1950)

10 9 10 10 D
GATHER US IN

9 Lord God Almighty

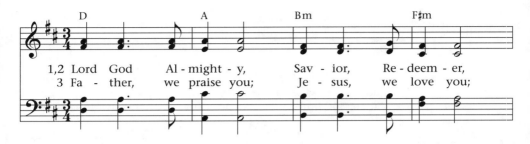

1,2 Lord God Al - might - y, Sav - ior, Re - deem - er,
3 Fa - ther, we praise you; Je - sus, we love you;

on - ly true God___ to be wor - shiped and praised:
Spir - it, we thank you for the gifts of new life.

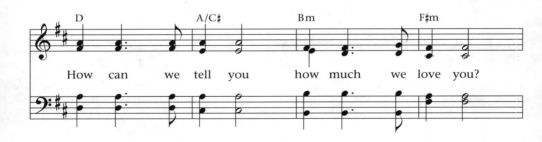

How can we tell you how much we love you?

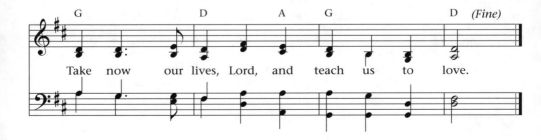

Take now our lives, Lord, and teach us to love.

Text and music: Coni Huisman (20th cent.)

© 1984, Coni Huisman

COMFORT

1 "Do not fear, for I have re-deemed you. You are mine, by name I have
called you. When you walk through the wa - ters, I will be there with
you. You are my wit-ness-es, cre - a - ted for my glo - ry. Tell the
na - tions I am the Sav - ior. Tell them I am the Lord."

2 Shout for joy, O heav - ens, and re - joice, O earth! In-to
joy - ful shout-ing let the moun - tains break forth! For the
Lord will com - fort his peo - ple, show com-pas-sion to those af - flict - ed.
He will not leave to shame those who trust in his Word.

D.C.

D.C. al Fine

From Varied Hills

10

Gathering From varied hills of daily cares and fields we till alone,
the Shepherd of all far flung life now gathers us as one.
Though soiled and empty, in this place we'll soon be washed and fed, re-

Parting God, send us forth in your own peace, according to your
Word; we have beheld salvation's power and shared in Christ, our Lord.
May we, bathed in your gospel light, help all the world to see. Help

Text: James Hart Brumm (b. 1962)
Music: Kathleen Hart Brumm (b. 1958); arr. Alfred V. Fedak (b. 1953)

CMD
BOOKENDS

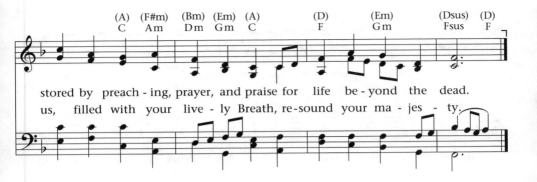

stored by preach - ing, prayer, and praise for life be - yond the dead.
us, filled with your live - ly Breath, re - sound your ma - jes - ty.

Be Still, for the Presence 11

1 Be still, for the pres-ence of the Lord, the Ho - ly One, is here.
2 Be still, for the glo - ry of the Lord is shin-ing all a - round.
3 Be still, for the pow - er of the Lord is mov-ing in this place.

Come bow be - fore him now, with rev - er - ence and fear.
He burns with ho - ly fire; with splen-dor he is crowned.
He comes to cleanse and heal, to min - is - ter his grace.

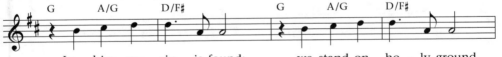

In him no sin is found; we stand on ho - ly ground.
How awe-some is the sight, our rad-iant King of light!
No work too hard for him; in faith re - ceive from him.

Be still, for the pres-ence of the Lord, the Ho - ly One, is here.
Be still, for the glo - ry of the Lord is shin-ing all a - round.
Be still, for the pow - er of the Lord is mov-ing in this place.

Text and music: David Evans (b. 1957)

12   We Bring the Sacrifice of Praise

We bring the sac - ri - fice of praise in - to the house of the Lord. We bring the sac - ri - fice of praise in - to the house of the Lord. And we of - fer up to you the sac - ri - fic - es of thanks - giv - ing, and we of - fer up to you the sac - ri - fic - es of praise.

Text and music: Kirk Dearman (b. 1952)

He Has Made Me Glad

Text and music: Leona Von Brethorst (b. 1923)

14 God, You Call Us to This Place

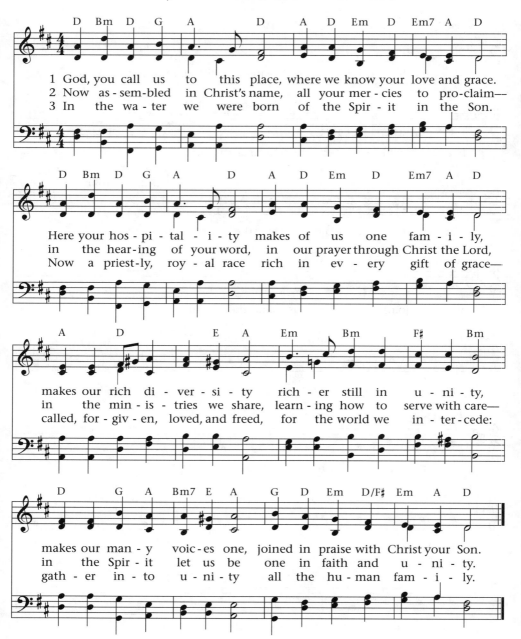

1 God, you call us to this place, where we know your love and grace.
2 Now as-sem-bled in Christ's name, all your mer-cies to pro-claim—
3 In the wa-ter we were born of the Spir-it in the Son.

Here your hos-pi-tal-i-ty makes of us one fam-i-ly,
in the hear-ing of your word, in our prayer through Christ the Lord,
Now a priest-ly, roy-al race rich in ev-ery gift of grace—

makes our rich di-ver-si-ty rich-er still in u-ni-ty,
in the min-is-tries we share, learn-ing how to serve with care—
called, for-giv-en, loved, and freed, for the world we in-ter-cede:

makes our man-y voic-es one, joined in praise with Christ your Son.
in the Spir-it let us be one in faith and u-ni-ty.
gath-er in-to u-ni-ty all the hu-man fam-i-ly.

Text: Delores Dufner (b. 1939)
Music: Jakob Hintze (1622-1702); harm. after Johann S. Bach (1685-1750)
Text © 1987, 1993, The Sisters of St. Benedict, admin. OCP Publications

77 77 D
SALZBURG

Psalm 24

Refrain Em   B7   Em

Lift up your head and let your heart hear the sto - ry:

B7   Em

Je - sus, the Lord al - might - y, is King of glo - ry.

Refrain

¹ The earth is the LORD's and all that is in it,
  the world, and those who live in it;
² **for he has founded it on the seas,**
  and established it on the rivers.

Refrain

³ Who shall ascend the hill of the LORD?
  And who shall stand in his holy place?
⁴ **Those who have clean hands and pure**
  hearts,
  who do not lift up their souls to what is
  false,
  and do not swear deceitfully.
⁵ They will receive blessing from the LORD,
  and vindication from the God of their
  salvation.

⁶ **Such is the company of those who seek**
  him,
  who seek the face of the God of Jacob.

Refrain

⁷ Lift up your heads, O gates!
  and be lifted up, O ancient doors!
  that the King of glory may come in.
⁸ Who is the King of glory?
  The LORD, strong and mighty,
  the Lord, mighty in battle.
⁹ Lift up your heads, O gates!
  and be lifted up, O ancient doors!
  that the King of glory may come in.
¹⁰ Who is this King of glory?
  The LORD of hosts,
  he is the King of glory.

Refrain

Alternate Refrain

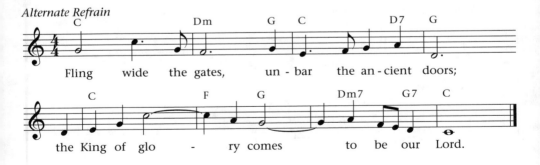

C   Dm   G   C   D7   G

Fling wide the gates, un - bar the an - cient doors;

C   F   G   Dm7   G7   C

the King of glo - ry comes to be our Lord.

Refrain text: Bert Polman (b. 1945)
Music: Israeli
Text © 2001, CRC Publications

PROMISED ONE

Alt. Refrain text: Michael Perry (1942-1996)
Music: Sydney H. Nicholson (1875-1947)
Ref. text © 1986, Jubilate Hymns Ltd., admin. Hope Publishing Co.; music © 1974, Hope Publishing Co.

CRUCIFER

16 I Love You, Lord

Step By Step

Descants

O God, you are my God, and I will ev-er praise

O God, you are my God, and I will ev-er praise

you. O God, you are my God, and I will ev-er praise

you. O God, you are my God, and I will ev-er praise

you. I will seek you in the morn - ing, and I will

you. I will seek you in the morn - ing, and I will

learn to walk in your ways. And step by step you'll lead

learn to walk in your ways. And step by step you'll lead

me, and I will fol-low you all of my days.

me, and I will fol-low you all of my days.

Text and music: Beaker (20th cent.)

© 1991, BMG Songs, Inc. (ASCAP)/Kid Brothers of St. Frank Publishing, admin. BMG Songs, Inc.

18 Jesus Is Our King

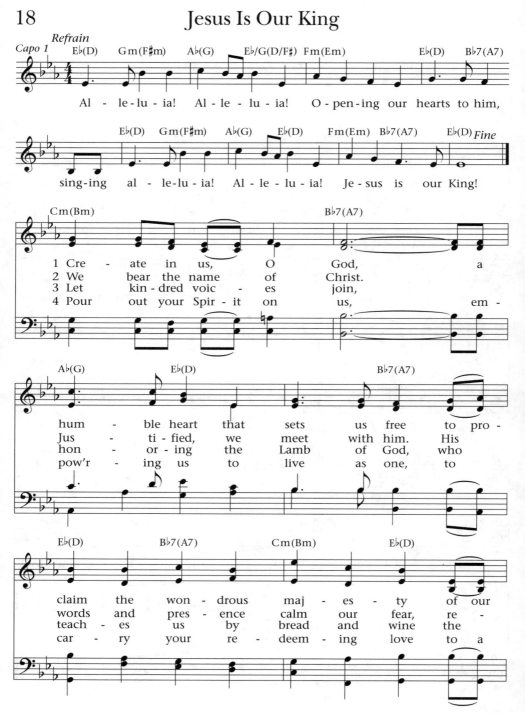

Text: Sherrell Prebble and Howard Page-Clark
Music: Sherrell Prebble

POST GREEN

© 1978, Celebration

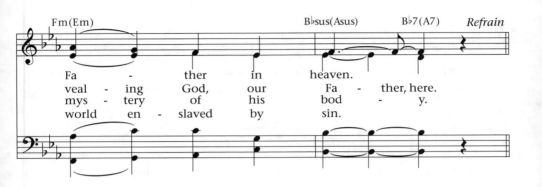

Fa - ther in heaven.
veal - ing God, our Fa - ther, here.
mys - tery of his bod - y.
world en - slaved by sin.

Santo, santo, santo, mi corazon / Holy, Holy, Holy, My Heart

19

Spanish San - to, san - to, san - to, mi cor - a - zon te a - do - ra!
English Ho - ly, ho - ly, ho - ly, my heart, my heart a - dores you!
Dutch Hei - lig, hei - lig, hei - lig, mijn hart brengt U de e - re!
French Dieu saint, Dieu saint, Dieu saint, mon coeur, mon coeur t'a - do - re.
Korean Gaw - rohk, gaw - rohk, gaw - rohk, nah - ruhl Ju - neem - ke drimnee - dah.

Mi cor - a - zon te sa - be de - cir: san - to e - res Se - ñor.
My heart pours out my praise to— you; you are ho - ly, Lord.
Van har - te loof ik U - we— Naam; hei - lig bent U, Heer.
Mon coeur le dit, mon coeur s'en ré - jouit: tu es saint, mon Dieu.
Nay - ga Ju - neem chan yahng hop-nee-dah; gaw - rohk hashin, Ju - neem.

Text and music: Spanish traditional; Eng. tr. *Sing! A New Creation* (2001); Dutch tr. Robert DeMoor (b. 1950); Fr. tr. Otto Selles (b. 1964); Korean tr. In Soon Gho (b. 1964); arr. Jorge Lockward (b. 1965)

20 You Are Holy / Eres santo

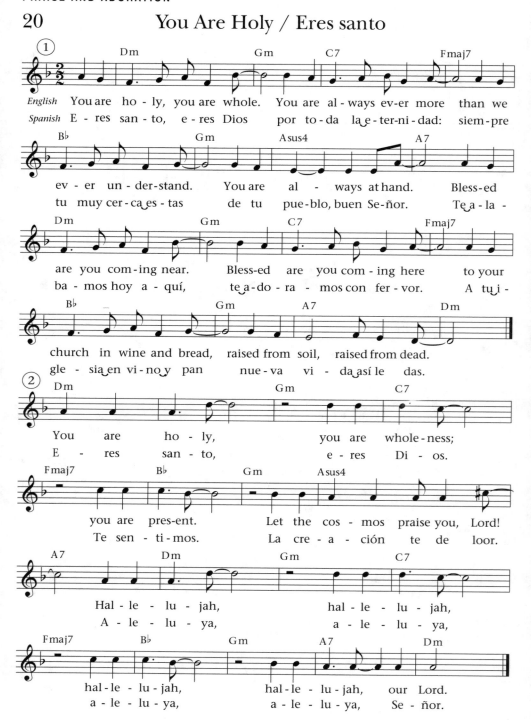

Text and music: Per Harling (b. 1945); Sp. tr. Raquel Gutiérrez-Achon (b. 1927)

DU AR HELIG

We Will Glorify

Text and music: Twila Paris (b. 1958); desc. Tom Fettke (b.1941)

22   Prayer for the Lord's Day

"Our help is in the name of the Lord,
who made heaven and earth." —Psalm 124:8

Let us pray.

Blessed are you, O God and Father
of our Lord Jesus Christ;
you have blessed us in Christ
with every spiritual blessing.

**Blessed are you, our God and Father;
you have destined us in love
to be your sons and daughters
in the person of your Son, Jesus Christ.**

You have freely bestowed
your grace upon us
in your beloved Son.

**You have made known to us
in all wisdom and insight
the mystery of your will,
the plan to unite all things in Christ.**

You have sealed us with the promised Holy
   Spirit,
the guarantee of our inheritance.

**Blessed are you, O God,
Father, Son, and Holy Spirit.
One God, forever and ever. Amen.**

23   Psalm 8

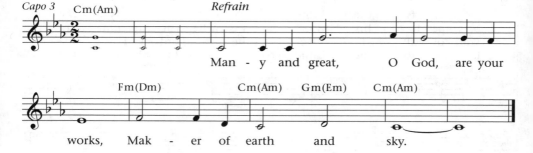

Refrain

¹ O LORD, our Sovereign,
   how majestic is your name in all the
   earth!

You have set your glory above the heavens.

² **Out of the mouths of babes and infants
  you have founded a bulwark because of
    your foes,
    to silence the enemy and the avenger.**
³ When I look at your heavens, the work of
    your fingers,
     the moon and the stars that you have
     established;

Refrain text: Joseph R. Renville (1779-1846); Eng. tr. Philip Frazier (1892-1964)
Music: Traditional Dakota

LACQUIPARLE

⁴ what are human beings that you are
   mindful of them,
   mortals that you care for them?
⁵ **Yet you have made them a little lower
   than God,
   and crowned them with glory and
   honor.**
⁶ You have given them dominion over the
   works of your hands;
   you have put all things under their feet,

⁷ all sheep and oxen,
   and also the beasts of the field,
⁸ the birds of the air, and the fish of the sea,
   **whatever passes along the paths of the
   seas.**
⁹ O LORD, our Sovereign,
   how majestic is your name in all the
   earth!

Refrain

How Majestic Is Your Name 24

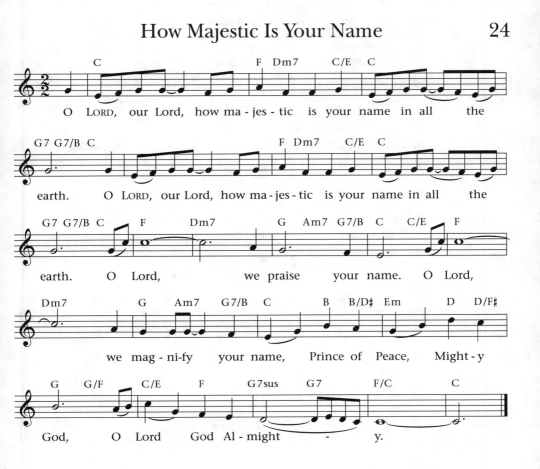

O LORD, our Lord, how ma - jes - tic is your name in all the earth. O LORD, our Lord, how ma - jes - tic is your name in all the earth. O Lord, we praise your name. O Lord, we mag - ni - fy your name, Prince of Peace, Might - y God, O Lord God Al - might - y.

Text and music: Michael W. Smith (b. 1957)
© 1981, Meadowgreen Music Company, admin. EMI Christian Music Publishing

25 Psalm 95: Come, Worship God

Text: Psalm 95; vers. Michael Perry (1942-1996)
Music: *Antiphoner*, Paris (1681); harm. John B. Dykes (1823-1876)

Text © 1980, Jubilate Hymns Ltd., admin. Hope Publishing Co.

11 10 11 10
O QUANTA QUALIA

Psalm 136: We Give Thanks unto You

Leader

Em   Am7   B7

1 We give thanks un - to you, O God of might,
2 In your wis - dom and love you shaped the skies,
3 You have filled all the skies with glo - ry and light,
4 From of old you have led your peo - ple in faith,
5 You de - liv - ered the ones who called un - to you,
6 You have o - pened the sea and brought your peo - ple through,
7 You re - mem - ber your pro - mise age to age,
8 You give food and life to all liv - ing things,

All

Em   B

for your love is nev - er end - ing;

Leader

B7   Em

1 we give thanks un - to you, the God of gods,
2 you spread out the earth up - on the sea,
3 the sun for the day and moon for night,
4 you have shown your com - pas - sion, strength, and love,
5 from bond - age to free - dom, you brought them forth,
6 brought them in - to a land that flows with life,
7 you show mer - cy on those of low de - gree,
8 we give thanks un - to you, the God of all,

All

G   Am   B7   Em

for your love is nev - er end - ing.

Text: Psalm 136; vers. Marty Haugen (b. 1950)
Music: Marty Haugen

27   Psalm 145

Spanish: Te e-xal-ta-ré, mi Dios, mi Rey, y ben-de-ci-ré tu nom-bre. E-ter-na-men-te y pa-ra siem-pre, ca-da dí-a te ben-de-ci-ré.

English: I will ex-alt my God, my King; I will praise your name for-ev-er. I will ex-alt your name for-ev-er; ev-ery day I'll praise your ho-ly name.

Refrain

¹ I will extol you, my God and King,
     and bless your name forever and ever.
² Every day I will bless you,
     and praise your name forever and ever.
³ **Great is the Lord, and greatly to be praised;**
     his greatness is unsearchable.
⁴ **One generation shall laud your works to another,**
     and shall declare your mighty acts.
⁵ On the glorious splendor of your majesty,
     and on your wondrous works, I will meditate.
⁶ The might of your awesome deeds shall be proclaimed,
     and I will declare your greatness.
⁷ **They shall celebrate the fame of your abundant goodness,**
     and shall sing aloud of your righteousness.

⁸ **The Lord is gracious and merciful,**
     slow to anger and abounding in steadfast love.

Refrain

⁹ The Lord is good to all,
     and his compassion is over all that he has made.
¹⁰ All your works shall give thanks to you, O Lord,
     and all your faithful shall bless you.
¹¹ **They shall speak of the glory of your kingdom,**
     and tell of your power,
¹² **to make known to all people your mighty deeds,**
     and the glorious splendor of your kingdom.
¹³ **Your kingdom is an everlasting kingdom,**
     and your dominion endures throughout all generations.

Refrain

Refrain: Casiodoro Cardenas (20th cent.)   ECUADOR

Psalm 146

Refrain

French Lou - ez le Sei-gneur! Lou - ez son saint nom. Al - le-lu - ia!

English Praise, praise, praise the Lord! Praise God's ho - ly name. Al - le-lu - ia!

Lou - ez le Sei-gneur! Lou - ez son saint nom. Al - le-lu - ia!

Praise, praise, praise the Lord! Praise God's ho - ly name. Al - le-lu - ia!

Lou - ez son saint nom. Al - le-lu - ia! Lou - ez son saint nom. Al - le-lu - ia!

Praise God's ho - ly name. Al-le-lu - ia! Praise God's ho - ly name. Al - le - lu-ia!

Lou - ez son saint nom. Al - le-lu - ia! Lou - ez son saint nom. Al - le - lu-ia!

Praise God's ho - ly name. Al - le - lu-ia! Praise God's ho - ly name. Al - le - lu-ia!

Refrain

¹ Praise the LORD!
  Praise the LORD, O my soul!
² **I will praise the LORD as long as I live;**
  I will sing praises to my God all my life
  long.
³ Do not put your trust in princes,
  in mortals, in whom there is no help.
⁴ When their breath departs, they return to
  the earth;
  on that very day their plans perish.

Refrain

⁵ Happy are those whose help is the God of
  Jacob,
  whose hope is in the LORD their God,
⁶ who made heaven and earth,

the sea, and all that is in them;
who keeps faith forever;
⁷ who executes justice for the oppressed;
  who gives food to the hungry.
The LORD sets the prisoners free;
⁸ **the LORD opens the eyes of the blind.**
  The LORD lifts up those who are bowed
  down;
  the LORD loves the righteous.
⁹ **The LORD watches over the strangers;**
  he upholds the orphan and the widow,
  but the way of the wicked he brings to
  ruin.
¹⁰The LORD will reign forever,
  your God, O Zion, for all generations.
Praise the LORD!

Refrain

Refrain: Cameroon processional; arr. Ralph M. Johnson (b. 1955)
Arr. © 1994, earthsongs

29   Psalm 147: Sing to God, with Joy

Text and music: John Bell (b. 1949), based on Psalm 147

© 1993, WGRG the Iona Community (Scotland), admin. GIA Publications, Inc.

87 87 with refrain
GLENDON

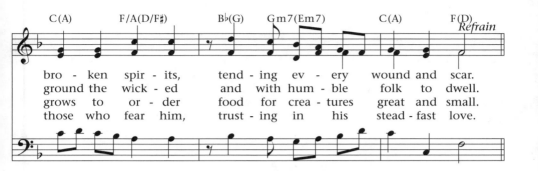

C(A)	F/A(D/F♯)	B♭(G)	Gm7(Em7)	C(A)	F(D) *Refrain*

bro - ken spir - its, tend - ing ev - ery wound and scar.
ground the wick - ed and with hum - ble folk to dwell.
grows to or - der food for crea - tures great and small.
those who fear him, trust - ing in his stead - fast love.

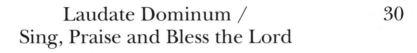

Laudate Dominum / 30
Sing, Praise and Bless the Lord

Latin Lau - da - te Do - mi - num, lau - da - te Do - mi - num
English Sing, praise and bless the Lord. Sing, praise and bless the Lord,

om - nes gen - tes! al - le - lu - ia! al - le - lu - ia!
peo - ples! na - tions! Al - le - lu - ia! Al - le - lu - ia!

31   Psalm 148

Let the whole cre - a - tion cry, Al - le - lu - ia!

Refrain

¹ Praise the LORD!
Praise the LORD from the heavens;
  praise him in the heights!
² **Praise him, all his angels;**
  praise him, all his host!
³ Praise him, sun and moon;
  praise him, all you shining stars!
⁴ **Praise him, you highest heavens,**
  and you waters above the heavens!
⁵ Let them praise the name of the LORD,
  for he commanded and they were
    created.
⁶ **He established them forever and ever;**
  he fixed their bounds, which cannot be
    passed.

Refrain

⁷ Praise the LORD from the earth,
  you sea monsters and all deeps,
⁸ fire and hail, snow and frost,
  stormy wind fulfilling his command!
⁹ **Mountains and all hills,**
  fruit trees and all cedars!
¹⁰**Wild animals and all cattle,**
  creeping things and flying birds!
¹¹Kings of the earth and all peoples,
  princes and all rulers of the earth!
¹²Young men and women alike,
  old and young together!
¹³**Let them praise the name of the LORD,**
  for his name alone is exalted;
  his glory is above earth and heaven.
¹⁴He has raised up a horn for his people,
  praise for all his faithful,
    for the people of Israel who are close to
      him.
Praise the LORD!

Refrain

Refrain text: *Sing! a New Creation*
Music: Robert Williams (1781-1821)

LLANFAIR

Psalm 150: Praise Ye the Lord

Praise ye the Lord, Hal-le-lu-jah! Ev-ery-bod-y praise the Lord.

1 Praise God with the sound of the trum-pet, praise God with the
2 Praise God—— with ho - ly cym-bals, praise God—— with
3 Praise God in the ho - ly tem-ple, praise God for al -
4 Praise God—— on top of the moun-tains, praise God—— both

lute and the harp; praise God—— with tim-brel and danc-
strings and with pipes; praise God—— with clash - ing cym-
might - y deeds; praise God for those boun-ti - ful mer-
day—— and night; praise God—— down in the low val-

ing, praise God wher - ev - er you are.
bals, praise God with all of your might.
cies, for God ful - fills—— our needs.
leys, praise God be - cause it's al - right.

Text and music: J. Jefferson Cleveland (1937-1986), based on Psalm 150

33 Sing a New Song to God

Refrain

Come, let us sing to the Lord; sing a new song to God!

Entrance	1 En - ter God's pres - ence; joy - ful wor - ship bring.
Praise	2 Praise our Cre - a - tor, Mak - er of heav'n and earth.
Confession	3 Lord God Al - might - y, par - don all our sin.
Thanksgiving	4 Praise to our Sav - ior who great deeds has done.

Praise God with mu - sic; pray and laugh and sing.
To God give glo - ry, God who gave us birth.
God of com - pas - sion, make us pure with - in.
Thanks to Christ Je - sus who our sal - va - tion won.

With thanks let us pon - der the won - der of life.
In awe let us pon - der the Source of our life.
Be gra - cious and an - swer, O hope of our life.
With joy let us pon - der the gift of New Life,

Refrain

Sing, shout prais - es to Yah - weh! Hal - le - lu - jah!
Sing, shout praise to our Mak - er! Hal - le - lu - jah!
O God, grant us for - give - ness! Hal - le - lu - jah!
sing, shout, praise our Re - deem - er! Hal - le - lu - jah!

Text: Donald H. Postema (b. 1934)
Music: Kevin J. Bylsma (b. 1965)
Text © 1990, Don Postema; music © 1990, Kevin Bylsma

10 10 11 11 with refrain
CAMPUS CHAPEL

Descant for final refrain

O let us sing! Come, let us sing to God; sing songs to God!

Come, let us sing to the Lord; sing a new song to God!

Advent/Christmas

5 Praise to Christ Jesus, Word of God made flesh;
born of a Virgin, full of grace and truth.
With Mary we ponder this Advent of Life.
Rejoice! Glory to God! Hallelujah!

Epiphany

6 Light of the nations, glorious Savior near,
our strength and refuge—who will make us fear?
Illumine our journey, O Sun of our life.
Glory, shine in our darkness. Hallelujah!

Lent

7 O Lord, have mercy, hear our urgent plea;
O Christ, have mercy, save us, set us free!
O crucified Savior, whose death gives us life,
bless us, cheer us with comfort; grant us your peace.

Easter

8 The Lord is risen! God has set us free.
The Lord is risen! Live triumphantly!
In gratitude savor new hope for our life.
Sing! Shout: "Christ is arisen! Hallelujah!"

Ascension

9 Praise to our Ruler, who makes hate to cease.
To God give honor, source of love and peace.
With hope let us follow the Lord of our life.
God reigns! Ruler Almighty! Hallelujah!

Pentecost

10 Come, Holy Spirit, strengthen us with your power.
O gentle Comfort, fill us with your peace.
Mysterious Presence, enlighten our life.
Guide us, Spirit of Wisdom. Hallelujah!

34   Let All Creation Bless the Lord

1 Let all cre - a - tion bless the Lord, till
2 All liv - ing things up - on the earth, green
3 O men and wom - en ev - ery - where, lift

heav'n with praise is ring - ing. Sun, moon, and stars, peal
fer - tile hills and moun - tains, sing to the God who
up a hymn of glo - ry; let all who know God's

out a chord, stir up the an - gels' sing - ing.
gave you birth; be joy - ful, springs and foun - tains.
stead - fast care tell out sal - va - tion's sto - ry.

Sing, wind and rain! Sing, snow and sleet! Make mu - sic, day, night,
Lithe wa - ter - life, bright air - borne birds, wild rov - ing beasts, tame
No tongue be sil - ent; sing your part, you hum - ble souls and

Text: Carl P. Daw, Jr. (b. 1944)
Music: Bohemian Brethren's *Kirchengesänge*, Berlin (1566); harm. Heinrich Reimann (19th cent.)

87 87 88 7
MIT FREUDEN ZART

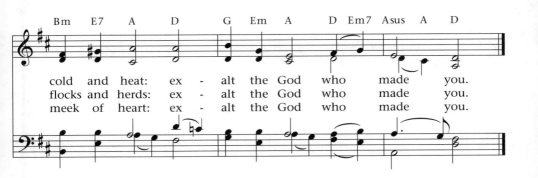

cold and heat: ex - alt the God who made you.
flocks and herds: ex - alt the God who made you.
meek of heart: ex - alt the God who made you.

O Praise the Gracious Power   35

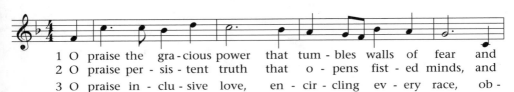

1 O praise the gra-cious power that tum-bles walls of fear and
2 O praise per-sis-tent truth that o-pens fist-ed minds, and
3 O praise in-clu-sive love, en-cir-cling ev-ery race, ob-
4 O praise the word of faith that claims us as God's own, a
5 O praise the tide of grace that laps at ev-ery shore with
6 O praise the power, the truth, the love, the Word, the tide; yet
7 O praise the liv-ing Christ with faith's bright song-ful voice! An-

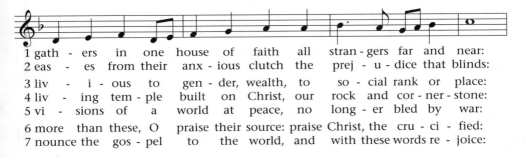

1 gath - ers in one house of faith all stran-gers far and near:
2 eas - es from their anx-ious clutch the prej-u-dice that blinds:
3 liv - i-ous to gen-der, wealth, to so-cial rank or place:
4 liv - ing tem-ple built on Christ, our rock and cor-ner-stone:
5 vi - sions of a world at peace, no long-er bled by war:
6 more than these, O praise their source: praise Christ, the cru-ci-fied:
7 nounce the gos-pel to the world, and with these words re-joice:

We praise you, Christ! Your cross has made us one!

Text: Thomas H. Troeger (b. 1945)
Music: Carol Doran (b. 1936)

SM with refrain
CHRISTPRAISE RAY

© 1994, Oxford University Press, Inc.

36 Creation Sings! Each Plant and Tree

1 Cre - a - tion sings! Each plant and tree, each bird and beast in har - mo - ny; the bright - est star, the small - est cell, God's ten - der care and glo - ry tell. From o - cean depths to moun - tain peaks, in praise of God, cre - a - tion speaks!

2 Cre - a - tion speaks a mes - sage true, re - minds us we are crea - tures too. To serve as stew - ards is our role, de - spite our dreams of full con - trol. When we dis - par - age what God owns, in tur - moil, all cre - a - tion groans.

3 Cre - a - tion groans to see the day that ends all bond - age, all de - cay. Frus - trat - ed now, it must a - wait the Lord who comes to re - cre - ate, till round the un - i - verse there rings the song God's new cre - a - tion sings!

Text: Martin E. Leckebusch (b. 1962)
Music: Dimitri S. Bortnianski (1751-1825)

Text © 1995, Kevin Mayhew Ltd.

88 88 88
ST. PETERSBURG

For the Music of Creation

1 For the mu-sic of cre-a-tion, for the song your Spir-it sings,
2 Psalms and sym-pho-nies ex-alt you, drum and trum-pet, string and reed.
3 All the voic-es of the a-ges in tran-scen-dent cho-rus meet,

for your sound's di-vine ex-pres-sion, burst of joy in liv-ing things:
Sim-ple mel-o-dies ac-claim you, tunes that rise from deep-est need,
wor-ship lift-ing up the sens-es, hands that praise, and danc-ing feet;

God, our God, the world's com-pos-er, hear us, ech-oes of your voice.
hymns of long-ing and be-long-ing, car-ols from a cheer-ful throat,
o-ver dis-cord and di-vi-sion mu-sic speaks your joy and peace,

Mu-sic is your art, your glo-ry; let the hu-man heart re-joice!
lilt of lul-la-by and love song catch-ing heav-en in a note.
har-mo-ny of earth and heav-en, song of God that can-not cease!

Text: Shirley Erena Murray (b. 1931)
Music: J. Wyeth's *Repository of Sacred Music* Part II (1813)

Text © 1992, Hope Publishing Co.

87 87 D
NETTLETON

38   Come, Praise God! Sing Hallelujah!

Refrain
Come, praise God! Sing hal - le - lu - jah! Come, praise the
ho - ly, al - migh-ty One. Come, know the Fa - ther in
Je - sus the Son. Raise joy-ful voi - ces, hal - le - lu - jah!

1 Hea - ven and earth make known God's power. How God has
2 Shout, all the earth! Lift voic - es, all! Come with thanks -

blessed us with - out end. Joined in a love that knows no bounds:
giv - ing, come with song. Play on the ti - fa, strike the drum!

Come! Praise with mel - o - dy, joy - ful and thank - ful!
Come! Praise with mel - o - dy, joy - ful and thank - ful!

Text and music: Subronto Kusumo Atmodjo (1929-1982; Indonesia); tr. Andrew Donaldson (b. 1951)   HALELUYA! PUJILAH

Tr. © 2001, Andrew Donaldson; music © 1988, *Kidung Jematt*

Alleluia, for the Lord God Almighty Reigns/ 39
Agnus Dei

Text and music: Michael W. Smith (b. 1957)

AGNUS DEI

40 Cantemos al Señor / O Sing unto the Lord

Spanish 1 Can-te-mos al Se-ñor un him-no de a-le-grí-a,
2 Can-te-mos al Se-ñor un him-no de a-la-ban-za

English 1 O sing un-to the Lord a hymn of cel-e-bra-tion;
2 O sing un-to the Lord a hymn of joy and prais-ing;

un cán-ti-co de a-mor al na-cer el nue-vo dí-a.
que ex-pre-se nues-tro a-mor, nues-tra fe y nues-tra es-pe-ran-za.
O sing a hymn of love, ev-ery day a new cre-a-tion.
a song that shares our love, our faith and hope-ful wait-ing.

Él hi-zo el cie-lo, el mar, el sol y las es-tre-llas
En to-da la crea-ción a-bun-da su gran-de-za;
God made the sky and sea, the sun and stars of heav-en
Cre-a-tion shouts to all that God is grand and glo-rious;

y en e-llos vio bon-dad, pues sus o-bras e-ran be-llas.
a-sí nues-tro can-tar va a-nun-cian-do su be-lle-za.
and saw that they were good; all cre-a-tion sings in splen-dor!
and so we sing our song to the God of grace and beau-ty.

Refrain

¡A-le-lu-ya! ¡A-le-lu-ya!
Al-le-lu-ia! Al-le-lu-ia!

Can-te-mos al Se-ñor. ¡A-le-lu-ya!
O sing to God a-bove: Al-le-lu-ia!

Text: Carlos Rosas (b. 1939); tr. C. Michael Hawn (b. 1948)
Music: Carlos Rosas

ROSAS
67 68 D with refrain

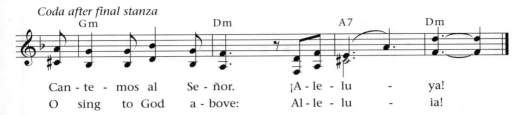

Coda after final stanza

Can - te - mos al Se - ñor. ¡A - le - lu - ya!
O sing to God a - bove: Al - le - lu - ia!

He Is Exalted

41

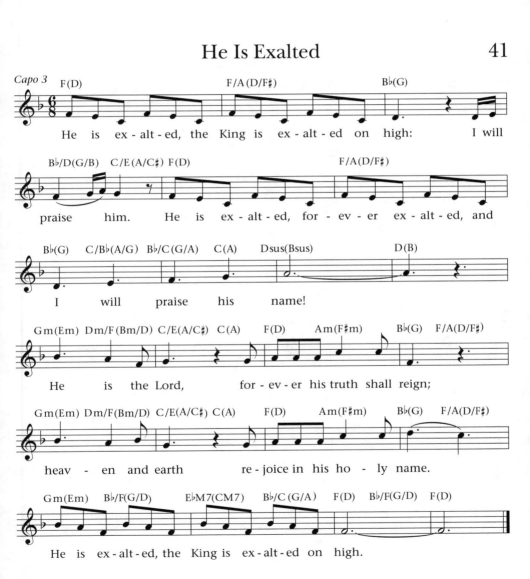

He is ex - alt - ed, the King is ex - alt - ed on high: I will

praise him. He is ex - alt - ed, for - ev - er ex - alt - ed, and

I will praise his name!

He is the Lord, for - ev - er his truth shall reign;

heav - en and earth re - joice in his ho - ly name.

He is ex - alt - ed, the King is ex - alt - ed on high.

Text and music: Twila Paris (b. 1958)

42

We Bow Down

1 You are Lord of cre-a-tion and Lord of my life, Lord of the land and the
2 You are King of cre-a-tion and King of my life, King of the land and the

sea; you were Lord of the heav - ens be - fore there was time, and
sea; you were King of the heav - ens be - fore there was time, and

Lord of all lords you will be. We bow down, and we
King of all kings you will be. We bow down, and we

wor - ship you, Lord; we bow down, and we wor-ship you, Lord; we bow
crown you the King; we bow down, and we crown you the King; we bow

Text and music: Twila Paris (b. 1958)

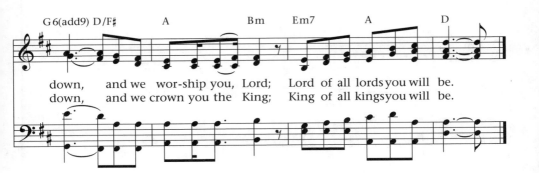

down, and we wor-ship you, Lord; Lord of all lords you will be.
down, and we crown you the King; King of all kings you will be.

Lord, Be Glorified

43

Text and music: Bob Kilpatrick (b. 1952)

44 Halle, Halle, Hallelujah!

Text: Marty Haugen (b. 1950)
Music: Caribbean; arr. John Bell (b. 1949) and Graham Maule (b. 1958)

Solo (sung over hummed refrain)

1 O God,—— to whom shall we go? You a-lone have the
2 My sheep hear my voice, says the Lord. When I call them, they

words of life. Let your words be our prayer and the
fol - low me. I will lead them to rest by the

song we sing: hal - le - lu-jah, hal - le - lu - jah.
peace - ful streams: hal - le - lu-jah, hal - le - lu - jah.

3 I am the light of the world, says the Lord. Walk in the

light of life. All who fol - low my words shall have

life in - deed: hal - le - lu-jah, hal - le - lu - jah.

Easter verse

4 Now Christ is raised up from death. He will nev - er

die a - gain. All who fol - low his way shall have

life in him: hal - le - lu-jah, hal - le - lu - jah.

You Are Author

45

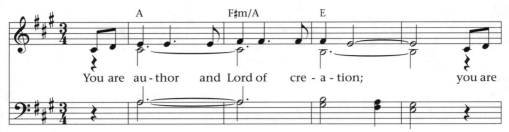

You are au-thor and Lord of cre-a-tion; you are

Note: Lower voices may vocalize parts on "Ah."

mak-er of life and of liv-ing. And from deep in our

hearts, won-der and love in-spire our wor-ship and praise.

Refrain

Hal - (hal) - le - lu-jah, hal - le - lu-

Text and music: Nepalese traditional as taught by Elisabeth Padillo-Oleson;
tr. WGRG the Iona Community (Scotland)

SARA SHRISTE

© 1990, Iona Community, admin. GIA Publications, Inc.

jah, hal - le - lu - jah, hal -

le - lu - jah. Hal - A - men.

Prayer of Praise to Our Creator   46

Creator God,
whose Spirit moved over the face of the
    waters,
who gathers the seas into their places
and directs the courses of the rivers,
who sends rain upon the earth that it
    should bring forth life:
We praise you for the gift of water.

Creator God,
whose hands shaped us out of the
dust of the earth,
who lifted up the mountains
and formed the dry land,
who formed the soil and made this earth
a place of beauty and abundance:
We praise you for the gift of soil.

Creator God,
whose Word called forth light from darkness,
who has robed this earth with a thin
    garment of air,
making it a haven of beauty and life,
who has breathed into each of us the
    breath of life:
We thank you for the gift of air.

**Create in us such a sense of wonder and
    delight
in these and all your gifts,
that we may receive them with gratitude,
care for them with love,
and generously share them with all your
    creatures,
to the honor and glory of your holy name.
Amen.**

47

Lord Most High

From the ends of the earth,
From the hearts of the weak,
From the ends of the earth,
hearts of the weak,
from the
from the

from the depths of the sea,
from the shouts of the strong,
depths of the sea,
shouts of the strong,
from the
from the

from the heights of the heav - ens your
from the lips of all peo - ple this
heights of the heav - ens
lips of all peo - ple
your
this

1. name be praised.
2. name be praised. From the
song we raise, Lord.
song we raise, Lord.

Text and music: Don Harris (b. 1959) and Gary Sadler (b. 1954)

48   # Praise Him! Jesus, Blessed Savior

1 Praise him, praise him, praise him,
2 Glo - ry! Glo - ry! In all things give him
3 Praise him, praise him, praise him,
4 Praise him, praise him, praise him,

praise him! Je - sus, bless-ed Sav - ior, he's
glo - ry. Je - sus, bless-ed Sav - ior, he's
praise him! Je - sus, bless-ed Sav - ior, he's
praise him! Je - sus, bless-ed Sav - ior, he's

wor - thy to be praised.   1 From the ris - ing of the
wor - thy to be praised.   2 For___ God___ is our
wor - thy to be praised.   3 From the ris - ing of the
wor - thy to be praised.

sun un - til the go - ing down of the same, he's wor - thy,
rock, hope of sal - va - tion; a strong___
sun un - til the go - ing down of the same, he's wor - thy,

Text and music: Donnie Harper (20th cent.)

Je - sus is wor - thy, he's wor - thy to___ be praised.
de - liv - er - er,___ in him I will al - ways trust.
Je - sus is wor - thy, he's wor - thy to___ be praised.

Create in Me a Clean Heart

49

Cre - ate in me a clean heart, O God, and re - new a right

spir - it with - in me. me. Cast me not a -

way from your pres - ence, O Lord, and take not your Ho - ly Spir - it from

me. Re - store un - to me the joy of your sal -

va - tion, and re - new a right spir - it with - in me.

Text and music: Anonymous, based on Psalm 51:10-12

50 Psalm 51

Refrain 1

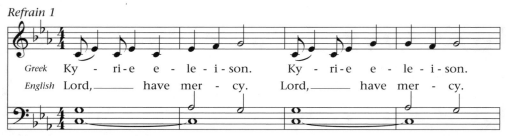

Note: Lower voices may hum.

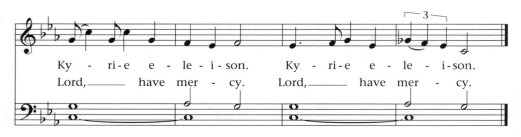

Refrain 1

¹ Have mercy on me, O God,
according to your steadfast love;
according to your abundant mercy
blot out my transgressions.

² Wash me thoroughly from my iniquity,
and cleanse me from my sin.

Refrain 1

⁴ᵃ Against you, you alone, have I sinned,
and done what is evil in your sight.

⁵ **Indeed, I was born guilty,**
a sinner when my mother conceived
me.

⁶ You desire truth in the inward being;
therefore teach me wisdom in my secret
heart.

Refrain 1

¹⁰ Create in me a clean heart, O God,
and put a new and right spirit within me.

¹¹ **Do not cast me away from your presence,**
and do not take your holy spirit from me.

¹² Restore to me the joy of your salvation,
and sustain in me a willing spirit.

Refrain 2 (see next page)

¹⁵ O Lord, open my lips,
and my mouth will declare your praise.

¹⁶ **For you have no delight in sacrifice;**
if I were to give a burnt offering, you
would not be pleased.

¹⁷ The sacrifice acceptable to God is a
broken spirit;
a broken and contrite heart, O God,
you will not despise.

Refrain 2

Refrain 1 text: early Greek liturgy
Music: Dinah Reindorf (b. 20th cent.), Ghana; arr. *Sing! A New Creation*

Music © 1987, Dinah Reindorf; arr. © 2001, CRC Publications

Refrain 2

Cre - ate in me a clean heart, O God,

and re-new a right spir-it with - in me.

Refrain 2 text: Psalm 51:10
Music: Anonymous

Shine on Me

51

Refrain
Capo 1

Shine on me, shine on me; Je - sus, shine on me.

Through the dark - ness of my heart, Je - sus, shine on me. *Fine*

1 See my heart, for I re - pent; hear my hum - ble plea
2 In your mer - cy I im-plore, make the dark-ness flee.
3 New be - gin - nings light my way toward e - ter - ni - ty.

to re - new your cov - e - nant. Je - sus, shine on me.
Heav'n - ly light up - on me pour. Je - sus, shine on me.
Lead me in your light to - day. Je - sus, shine on me. *Refrain*

Text and music: Richard K. Carlson (b.1956)
© 1989, Hark! Productions, Inc.

52   Prayer of Confession 1

Merciful God,
we confess that we have sinned against you
in thought, word and deed,
by what we have done,
and by what we have left undone.
We have not loved you
with our whole heart and mind and
    strength.
We have not loved our neighbors as
    ourselves.

In your mercy forgive what we have been,
help us amend what we are,
and direct what we shall be,
so that we may delight in your will
and walk in your ways,
to the glory of your holy name.

All sing:

Text: early Greek
Music: Russian Orthodox liturgy

Assurance of Pardon

Who is in a position to condemn?
Only Christ,
and Christ died for us,
Christ rose for us,
Christ reigns in power for us,
Christ prays for us.

Anyone who is in Christ is a new creation.
The old life has gone; a new life has begun.

Believe the good news of the gospel:
In Jesus Christ we are forgiven.

    —from Romans 8:34 and 2 Corinthians 5:17

Response

All sing a hymn or psalm of praise.

Prayer of Confession 2

Gracious God,
our sins are too heavy to carry,
too real to hide,
and too deep to undo.
Forgive what our lips tremble to name,
what our hearts can no longer bear,
and what has become for us
a consuming fire of judgment.

Set us free from a past
that we cannot change;
open us to a future
in which we can be changed;
and grant us grace
to grow more and more
in your likeness and image;
through Jesus Christ, the light of the world.

All sing:

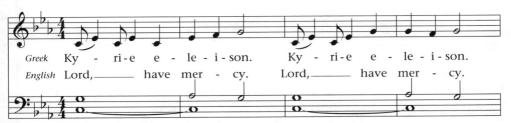

Greek Ky - ri-e e - le - i - son. Ky - ri-e e - le - i - son.
English Lord,——— have mer - cy. Lord,——— have mer - cy.

Note: Lower voices may hum.

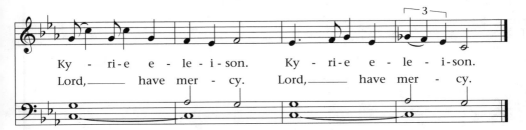

Ky - ri-e e - le - i - son. Ky - ri-e e - le - i - son.
Lord,——— have mer - cy. Lord,——— have mer - cy.

Text: early Greek liturgy
Music: Dinah Reindorf (b. 20th cent.), Ghana; arr. *Sing! A New Creation*
Music © 1987, Dinah Reindorf; arr. © 2001, CRC Publications

Assurance of Pardon

This saying is sure and worthy of full
acceptance:
Christ Jesus came into the world to save
sinners.
He bore our sins in his body on the cross,
so that free from sins,

we might live for righteousness.
By his wounds we have been healed.
—from 1 Timothy 1:15 and 1 Peter 2:24

Believe this good news and live in peace.

Response

All sing a hymn or psalm of praise.

54

Kyrie

Ky - ri-e. Lord, have mer-cy.

All Ky - ri-e. Lord, have mer-cy.

Chris - te. Christ, have mer - cy.

Chris - te. Christ, have mer - cy.

Ky - ri-e! Lord, have mer - cy.

Ky - ri-e. Lord, have mer - cy.

Ky - ri-e, e - le - i-son.

Ky - ri-e, e - le - i-son.

Text and music: Kathleen Hart Brumm (b. 1958)

Prayer of Confession 3

Call to Confession

Remember that our Lord Jesus Christ
is able to sympathize with us in our
weaknesses.
In every respect he was tempted as we are,
yet without sin.
Let us therefore approach the throne of
grace with boldness,
so that we may receive mercy
and find grace to help in time of need.

—Hebrews 4:15-16

Let us confess our sins to Almighty God.

Prayer of Confession

Refrain ("Kyrie," 54)

Most merciful God,
whose son Jesus Christ was tempted in
every way, yet without sin,
we confess before you our own
sinfulness:
we have hungered after that which
does not satisfy;

we have compromised with evil;
we have doubted your power to
protect us.
Forgive our lack of faith;
have mercy on our weakness.
Restore in us such trust and love
that we may walk in your ways
and delight in doing your will.

Refrain

Assurance of Pardon

Those who love me, I will deliver, says the
Lord;
I will protect those who know my name.
When they call to me, I will answer them;
I will be with them in trouble,
I will rescue them and honor them.
With long life I will satisfy them,
and show them my salvation.

—Psalm 91:14-16

Receive the good news of the gospel:
In Jesus Christ we are forgiven. Alleluia!

All sing:

Al-le - lu - ia! Al-le-lu - ia! In Je-sus Christ we are for-given!

Text and music: Joy F. Patterson (b. 1931)

56 Cámbiame, Señor / Change My Heart, O God

Spanish Cám - bia - me, Se - ñor, con tu gran po - der.
English Change my heart, O God; make it ev - er true.

Haz - me co - mo tú, tu - yo quie - ro ser.
Change my heart, O God; may I be like you.

Tú el al - fa - re - ro, yo el ba - rro soy.
You are the Pot - ter; I am the clay.

Só - lo a tu i - ma - gen, quie - ro siem - pre ser.
Mold me and make me; this is what I pray.

Text and music: Eddie Espinosa (b. 1953)

Come, Let Us Reason

Text and music: Ken Medema (b. 1943); arr. David Allen (b. 1941)

COME LET US REASON

58   Children from Your Vast Creation

1 Chil - dren from your vast cre - a - tion gath - er
2 We have grasped for more pos - ses - sions, want - ing
3 We are learn - ing how much dam - age spreads through-
4 Lord, we come as sis - ters, broth - ers, seek - ing

here for guid - ance, Lord; we of ev - ery tongue and
things we do not need; help us, Lord, lest our ob -
out the world from greed; though you made us in your
your re - demp - tive touch. Let un - self - ish love for

na - tion yearn to see your earth re - stored.
ses - sions soon con - sume us in our greed.
im - age, we are less than you de - creed.
oth - ers tri - umph, lest we want too much.

Text: David A. Robb (b. 1932)
Music: William P. Rowlands (1860-1937)
Text © 1997, Selah Publishing Co., Inc.

87 87 D
BLAENWERN

59 Perdón, Señor / Forgive Us, Lord

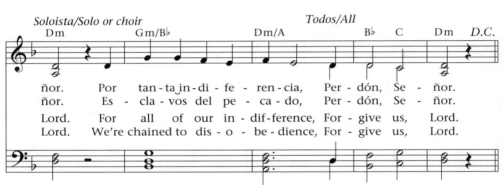

Spanish soloista

3 Al perdonar a otros, . . .
   De_acuerdo_a tu promesa, . . .

4 Libera hoy tu pueblo, . . .
   Que pueda hoy servirte, . . .

English solo or choir

3 As we forgive each other, . . .
   According to your promise, . . .

4 Deliver us from evil, . . .
   For joyful service free us, . . .

Text and music: Jorge Lockward (b. 1965)

4 74 74
CONFESION

Psalm 50: Let God, Who Called the Worlds to Be

1 Let God, who called the worlds to be, a-rise in all-con-sum-ing fire to judge the peo-ple righ-teous-ly, and faith-less ones with awe in-spire.

2 This God is ours, and yet we break the cov-e-nant made long a-go. God's words we fool-ish-ly for-sake; God's ways we have re-fused to know.

3 For though our lips have preached God's law, our err-ing hearts have scorned the name. We choose the thief and slan-der-er as friends, and so in-crease our shame.

4 What then shall God the Lord de-mand? Not gifts or lav-ish of-fer-ing, but vows and prom-is-es per-formed, and lives from which true prais-es spring!

Descant
but prom-is-es per-formed, and lives from which true prais-es spring!

Text: Psalm 50; vers. David Mowbray (b. 1938)
Music: *Second Supplement to Psalmody in Miniature* (c. 1780); arr. Edward Miller (1731-1807);
   desc. Betty Pulkingham (b. 1928)

Text © 1990, Jubilee Hymns Ltd., admin. Hope Publishing Co.; desc. © 1979, Celebration

LM
ROCKINGHAM

61 In An Age of Twisted Values

Capo 1

(Em) (Bm) (Em) (D) (G) (D)
Fm Cm Fm E♭ A♭ E♭

1 In an age of twist - ed val-ues we have lost the
2 We have built dis - crim - i - na-tion on our prej - u -
3 When our fam - i - lies are bro-ken, when our homes are
4 We who hear your word so of-ten choose so rare - ly

(Em) (A) (B) (Em) (Bm) (Em) (D)
Fm B♭ C Fm Cm Fm E♭

truth we need. In so - phis - ti - ca - ted lan-guage
dice and fear. Ha - tred swift - ly turns to cru-el - ty
full of strife, when our chil - dren are be - wil-dered,
to o - bey. Turn us from our will - ful blind-ness;

(G) (A/C♯) (D) (Em) (Bm) (Em) (D) (D)
A♭ B♭/D E♭ Fm Cm Fm D♭ E♭

we have jus - ti - fied our greed. By our strug - gle
if we hold re - sent - ments dear. For com - mu - ni -
when they lose their way in life, when we fail to
give us truth to light our way. In the pow - er

(G) (C) (D) (Am) (Bm) (Em) (A) (Bsus) (B) (Em)
A♭ D♭ E♭ B♭m Cm Fm B♭ Csus C Fm

for pos - ses - sions we have robbed the poor and weak. Hear our
ties di - vi - ded by the walls of class and race, hear our
give the ag - ed all the care we know they need, hear our
of your Spir - it come to cleanse us, make us new; hear our

(Bm) (Em) (D) (G) (Am) (Bm7) (C) (Am) (Bm7) (Em)
Cm Fm E♭ A♭ B♭m Cm7 D♭ B♭m Cm7 Fm

cry and heal our na-tion; your for - give - ness, Lord, we seek.
cry and heal our na-tion; show us, Lord, your love and grace.
cry and heal our na-tion; help us show more love, we plead.
cry and heal our na-tion till our na - tion hon - ors you.

Text: Martin E. Leckebusch (b. 1962)
Music: Alfred V. Fedak (b. 1953)
Alternate tune: BEACH SPRING, 153

87 87 D
CHURCH UNITED

Psalm 130: In Deep Despair I Cry to You 62

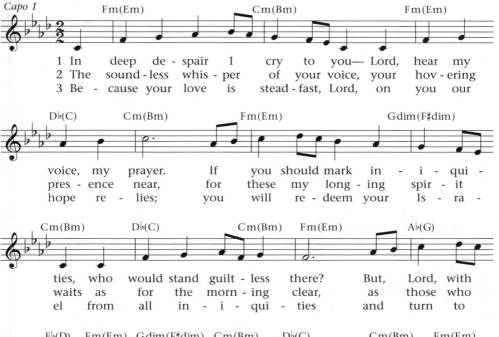

1 In deep de-spair I cry to you— Lord, hear my
2 The sound-less whis-per of your voice, your hov-ering
3 Be-cause your love is stead-fast, Lord, on you our

voice, my prayer. If you should mark in-i-qui-
pres-ence near, for these my long-ing spir-it
hope re-lies; you will re-deem your Is-ra-

ties, who would stand guilt-less there? But, Lord, with
waits as for the morn-ing clear, as those who
el from all in-i-qui-ties and turn to

you for-give-ness dwells and love be-yond com-pare.
watch through-out the night till morn-ing shall ap-pear.
songs of thanks and praise our sor-row and our sighs.

Text: Psalm 130; para. Joy F. Patterson (b. 1931)
Music: *Sixteen Tune Settings* (1812)
Text © 1994, Selah Publishing Co., Inc.

86 86 86
MORNING SONG

63 Who Can Sound the Depths of Sorrow

Capo 1:

Bb(A)   F(E)   Eb(D) Bb(A)   Gm(F#m)

All   1 Who can sound the depths of sor-row in the lov-ing
All   2 We have scorned the truth you gave us, we have bowed to
Men   3 Who can stand be-fore your an-ger? Who can face your
Women 4 Who will stand a-gainst the vio-lence? Who will com-fort
All   5 Who can sound the depths of mer-cy in the lov-ing

Dm(C#m)   Eb(D)   F(E)   Bb(A)   Gm(F#m)

heart of God, for the child-ren we've re-ject-ed, for the
oth-er lords, we have sac-ri-ficed the child-ren on the
pier-cing eyes? For you love the weak and help-less, and you
those who mourn? In an age of cruel re-jec-tion, who will
heart of God? For there is a Man of Sor-row, who for

C7(B7)   Fsus(Esus) F(E)   Bb(A)   F(E)

lives so deep-ly scarred? And each light that we've ex-
al-tars of our gods. O let truth a-gain shine
hear the vic-tim's cries. *All* Yes, you are a God of
build for love a home? *All* Come and shake us in-to
sin-ners shed his blood. He can heal the wounds of

Eb(D) Bb(A)   Gm(F#m)   Dm(C#m)   Eb(D)   A7(G#7)

tin-guished has brought dark-ness to our land. Up-on our
on us; let your ho-ly fear de-scend. Up-on our
jus-tice, and your judg-ment sure-ly comes. Up-on our
ac-tion, come and melt our hearts of stone. Up-on your
na-tions; he can wash the guil-ty clean. Be-cause of

Bb(A)   Gb(F)   Bb(A)   Fsus(Esus) F(E)   Bb(A)

na-tion, up-on our na-tion, have mer-cy, Lord.
na-tion, up-on our na-tion, have mer-cy, Lord.
na-tion, up-on our na-tion, have mer-cy, Lord.
peo-ple, up-on your peo-ple, have mer-cy, Lord.
Je-sus, be-cause of Je-sus, have mer-cy, Lord.

Text and music: Graham Kendrick (b. 1950), based on Psalm 12 and 82

© 1988, Make Way Music, admin. Music Services

Give Me a Clean Heart

Give me a clean heart so I may serve you. Lord, fix my

heart so that I may be used by you. For I'm not

wor - thy of all these bless - ings. Give me a

clean heart and I'll fol-low you. 1 I'm not
(2 Some-times)

ask - ing for the rich - es of the land. I'm not
I am up and some-times I am down. Some-times

ask - ing for the proud to know my name. Please
I am al - most lev - el to the ground.

give me, Lord, a clean heart, that I may fol - low you. Give me a

clean heart, a clean heart and I will fol-low you. 2 Some-times

Text and music: Margaret J. Douroux (b. 1941)
© 1970, Earl Pleasant Publishing

65 Listen, God Is Calling

Refrain

Lis - ten, lis-ten, God is call-ing, through the Word in - vit-ing,
of - fer-ing for - give-ness, com - fort and joy. joy.

1 Je - sus gave his man-date: share the good news
2 Let none be for - got - ten through - out the world.
3 Help us to be faith - ful, stand - ing stead - fast,

that he came to save us; he set us free.
Go to ev - ery na - tion, go and bap - tize.
walk-ing in your foot-steps, led by your Word.

Text and music: Tanzanian traditional; tr. Howard S. Olson (b. 1922); arr. C. Michael Hawn (b. 1948)
Tr. © 1979, Lutheran Theological College, Makumira, Tanzania, admin. Augsburg Fortress

64 64 with refrain
NENO LAKE MUNGU

For Freedom Christ Has Set Us Free! 66

1 For free-dom Christ has set us free! Do
2 But still so close-ly clings the sin that
3 Christ's free-dom works with-in our lives like
4 So faith, ex-pressed through love, be-comes the

not sub-mit a - gain to yokes of bond - age,
wears a - way our hope; faint heart and faith - less -
yeast works in the dough; then shack-les break and
Spir - it's fruit - ful tree, a new cre - a - tion

cells of doubt, or slav-ery's bit - ter chain.
ness and fear be - come our chain and yoke.
bur - dens fall, life ris - es, heal - ing shows.
in this world to set the cap - tives free.

Text: Sylvia Dunstan (1955-1993), based on Galatians 5
Music: Carl Glazer (1784-1829)

86 86
AZMON

67   Psalm 81

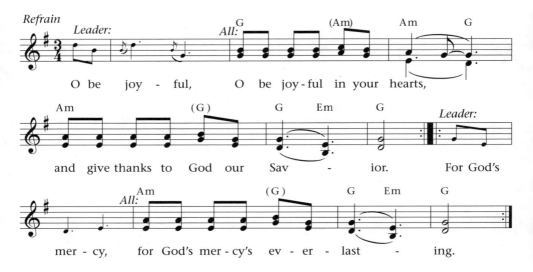

Refrain

Voice One

¹ Sing aloud to God our strength;
   shout for joy to the God of Jacob.
² Raise a song, sound the tambourine,
   the sweet lyre with the harp.
³ Blow the trumpet at the new moon,
   at the full moon, on our festal day.
⁴ For it is a statute for Israel,
   an ordinance of the God of Jacob.
⁵ He made it a decree in Joseph,
   when he went out over the land of Egypt.

Refrain

Voice One
I hear a voice I had not known:

Voice Two
⁶ "I relieved your shoulder of the burden;
   your hands were freed from the basket.
⁷ In distress you called, and I rescued you;
   I answered you in the secret place of
     thunder;
   I tested you at the waters of Meribah.

⁸ Hear, O my people, while I admonish you;
   O Israel, if you would but listen to me!
⁹ There shall be no strange god among you;
   you shall not bow down to a foreign god.
¹⁰ I am the LORD your God,
   who brought you up out of the land of
     Egypt.
   Open your mouth wide and I will fill
     it."

Refrain

Voice Two
¹³ "O that my people would listen to me,
   that Israel would walk in my ways!
¹⁴ Then I would quickly subdue their
     enemies,
   and turn my hand against their foes.
¹⁶ I would feed you with the finest of the
     wheat,
   and with honey from the rock I would
     satisfy you."

Refrain

Refrain: Malawian traditional; tr. Clara Henderson (b. 1955)

NDIMITIMA

Your Mercy Flows

Text and music: Wes Sutton (b. 1955)

© 1988, Sovereign Lifestyle Music

69 We Cannot Measure How You Heal

1 We can - not meas - ure how you heal or an - swer ev - ery
2 The pain that will not go a - way, the guilt that clings from
3 So some have come who need your help and some have come to

suf - ferer's prayer, yet we be - lieve your grace re -
things long past, the fear of what the fu - ture
make a - mends, as hands which shaped and saved the

sponds where faith and doubt u - nite to care. Your
holds, are pres - ent as if meant to last. But
world are pres - ent in the touch of friends. Lord,

hands, though blood - ied on the cross, sur - vive to
pres - ent too is love which tends the hurt we
let your Spir - it meet us here to mend the

Text: John L. Bell (b. 1949)
Music: Scottish traditional; arr. Iona Community

LMD
YE BANKS AND BRAES

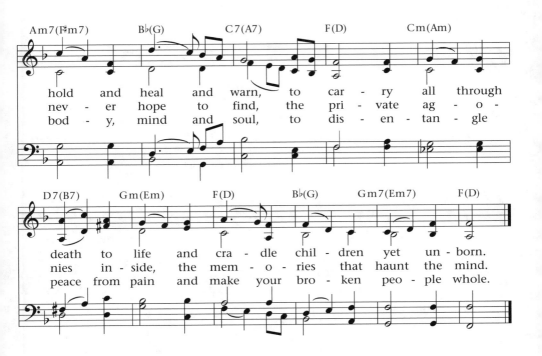

hold and heal and warn, to car - ry all through
nev - er hope to find, the pri - vate ag - o -
bod - y, mind and soul, to dis - en - tan - gle

death to life and cra - dle chil - dren yet un - born.
nies in - side, the mem - o - ries that haunt the mind.
peace from pain and make your bro - ken peo - ple whole.

I Will Give You Rest

70

"I will give you rest for your wear - y soul.

If you on - ly come to me I will make you whole."

Text and music: Barbara Boertje (b. 1959), based on Matt. 11:28-29
© 1996, Barbara Boertje

71

Good To Me

I cry out for your hand of mer-cy to heal me.

I am weak; I need your love to free me. O

Lord, my rock, my strength in weak-ness, come

res - cue me, O Lord. You are my

hope; your pro - mise ne - ver fails me. And my de -

sire is to fol - low you for - e - ver. For you are

good, for you are good, for you are good to me. For you are

good, for you are good, for you are good to me.

Text and music: Craig Musseau (b. 1965)

I'm So Glad Jesus Lifted Me

1 I'm so glad
2 Satan had me bound;
3 When I was in trouble,

Je-sus lift-ed me.

I'm so glad
Satan had me bound;
When I was in trouble,

Je-sus lift-ed me.

I'm so glad
Satan had me bound;
When I was in trouble,

Je-sus lift-ed me, sing-ing

glo-ry, hal-le-lu-jah! Je-sus lift-ed me.

Text and music: African-American spiritual

JESUS LIFTED ME

73 The Lord Is God, the One and True God

1 The Lord is God, the one and true God, be-yond all
2 Fa-ther and moth-er we will hon-or; all hu-man
3 Truth-ful in speech, our rep-u-ta-tion; by self-less-

we can think or see. God's name a-mong us shall be
life will we be-friend. All whom we love will find us
ness shall we be known. Un-end-ing love we pledge all

ho-ly. God's Sab-bath rest shall make us free.
faith-ful; our neigh-bor's goods will we de-fend.
peo-ple, our high-est love for God a-lone.

Text: The Ten Commandments; para. Daniel J. Meeter (b. 1953)
Music: Genevan Psalter (1547); harm. Claude Goudimel (c. 1505-1572)
Text © 1980, Daniel J. Meeter

98 98
COMMANDMENTS

Surely It Is God Who Saves Me

Refrain

Sure-ly it is God who saves me; I will trust in him and
not be a-fraid. For the Lord is my strong-hold and my
sure de-fense, and he will be my Sav-ior.

1 Therefore you shall draw water with rejoicing
   from the springs of salvation.
   And on that day you shall say,
   give thanks to the Lord and call upon his name.   *Refrain*

2 Make his deeds known among the peoples;
   see that they remember that his name is exalted.
   Sing the praises of the Lord, for he has done great things,
   and this is known in all the world.   *Refrain*

3 Cry aloud, inhabitants of Zion; ring out your joy,
   for the great one in the midst of you is the Holy One of Israel.   *Refrain*

Text: *The Book of Common Prayer*, based on Isaiah 12:3-6
Music: Jack Noble White (20th cent.)

Music © 1977, The H. W. Gray Company, admin. Warner Bros. Publications U.S., Inc.

FIRST SONG OF ISAIAH

75 Beyond the Beauty and the Awe

Descant

5 Then help us live as Je - sus taught, as

F C sus C F Dm B♭6 C F

1 Be - yond the beau - ty and the awe, be -
2 Our lives feel torn be - tween the world, whose
3 Oh, teach us how to hear your voice de -
4 In sound or si - lence, sight or smell, may
5 Then help us live as Je - sus taught, as

light and salt and yeast, that oth - ers may be

B♭/D F B♭ B♭6 A F B♭/D C C6

yond the fear and dread, we long, O God, to
needs are grim - ly real, and emp - ty talk of
spite the traf - fic's din, to keep the blasts of
we some tok - en find that makes your liv - ing
light and salt and yeast, that oth - ers may be

brought to share your prom - ise and your feast.

Dm C F C Dm Gm/B♭ C F

hear your word, to taste your trans - formed bread.
peace and joy with dis - tant, vague ap - peal.
ran - cor out and let your Spir - it in.
pres - ence known to bod - y, soul, and mind.
brought to share your prom - ise and your feast.

Text: Carl P. Daw, Jr. (b. 1944)
Music: J. Day's *Psalter* (1562); desc. Alan Gray (1855-1935)
Text © 1994, Hope Publishing Co.

CM
ST. FLAVIAN

Prayers for Illumination

1

Guide us, O Lord, by your Word and Holy Spirit,
that in your light we may see light,
in your truth find freedom,
and in your will discover peace;
through Jesus Christ our Lord.

2

Eternal God,
in the reading of Scripture may your Word be heard;
in the meditation of our hearts, may your Word be known;
in the faithfulness of our lives, may your will be done.

3

Come, Light, Light of God, o'er-whelm all cre - a - tion.

En - light - en our hearts; let your light dwell with us.

Text and music: The Sisters of the Community of Grandchamp, Switzerland; tr. Bert Polman (b. 1945);
    arr. Emily R. Brink (b. 1940)

77　I Want to Walk as a Child of the Light

1 I want to walk as a child of the light;
2 I want to see the bright - ness of God;
3 I'm look - ing for the com - ing of Christ;

I want to fol - low Je - sus.
I want to look at Je - sus.
I want to be with Je - sus.

God set the stars to give light to the world;
Clear Sun of righ - teous - ness, shine on my path,
When we have run with pa - tience the race,

the star of my life is Je - sus.
and show me the way to the Fa - ther.
we shall know the joy of Je - sus.

Text and music: Kathleen Thomerson (b. 1934)
© 1970, 1975, Celebration

10 7 10 8 with refrain
HOUSTON

Refrain

In him there is no dark - ness at all;
the night and the day are both a - like.
The Lamb is the light of the cit - y of God;
shine in my heart, Lord Je - sus.

78 God the Sculptor of the Mountains

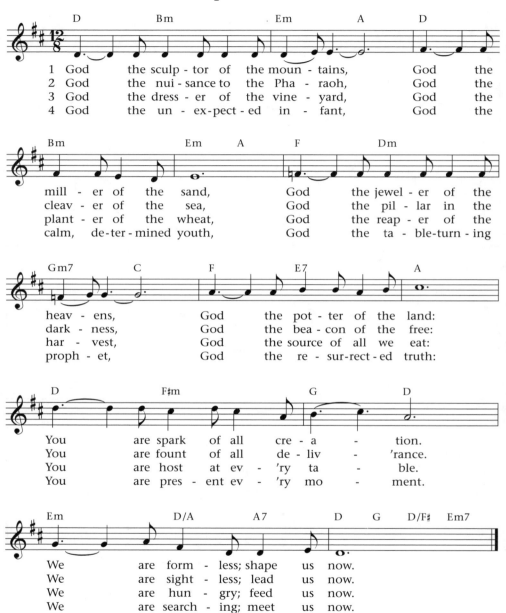

1 God the sculp - tor of the moun - tains,
2 God the nui - sance to the Pha - raoh,
3 God the dress - er of the vine - yard,
4 God the un - ex - pect - ed in - fant,

God the
God the
God the
God the

mill - er of the sand, God the jewel - er of the
cleav - er of the sea, God the pil - lar in the
plant - er of the wheat, God the reap - er of the
calm, de - ter - mined youth, God the ta - ble-turn - ing

heav - ens, God the pot - ter of the land:
dark - ness, God the bea - con of the free:
har - vest, God the source of all we eat:
proph - et, God the re - sur-rect - ed truth:

You are spark of all cre - a - tion.
You are fount of all de - liv - 'rance.
You are host at ev - 'ry ta - ble.
You are pres - ent ev - 'ry mo - ment.

We are form - less; shape us now.
We are sight - less; lead us now.
We are hun - gry; feed us now.
We are search - ing; meet us now.

Text: John Thornburg (b. 1954)
Music: Amanda Husberg (b. 1940)
Text © 1993, John Thornburg; music © 1996, Abingdon Press, admin. The Copyright Company

87 87 87
JENNINGS-HOUSTON

Lord, Let My Heart Be Good Soil

Lord, let my heart be good soil, o-pen to the seed of your Word. Lord, let my heart be good soil, where love can grow and peace is un-der-stood. When my heart is hard, break the stone a-way. When my heart is cold, warm it with the day. When my heart is lost, lead me on your way. Lord, let my heart, Lord, let my heart, Lord, let my heart be good soil.

Text and music: Handt Hanson (b. 1950)

© 1985, Prince of Peace Publishing/Changing Church, Inc.

GOOD SOIL

80 Open Our Eyes, Lord

Text and music: Robert Cull (b. 1949); arr. David Allen (b. 1941)
© 1976, Maranatha Music, admin. The Copyright Company

11 12 11 11
OPEN OUR EYES

Cry of My Heart

Text and music: Terry Butler (b. 1955)

© 1991, Mercy/Vineyard Publishing, admin. Music Services

82 Prayer for Blessing Following the Sermon

**Almighty God, grant that the words we have heard this day may,
through your grace, be so grafted within our hearts
that they may bring forth in us the fruit of the Spirit,
to the honor and praise of your name;
through Jesus Christ our Lord.
Amen.**

83 Many and Great

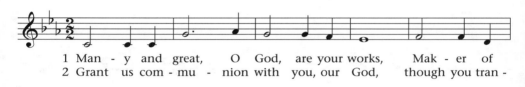

1 Man - y and great, O God, are your works, Mak - er of
2 Grant us com - mu - nion with you, our God, though you tran -

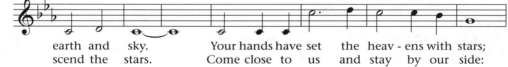

earth and sky. Your hands have set the heav - ens with stars;
scend the stars. Come close to us and stay by our side:

your fin - gers spread the moun - tains and plains. You mere - ly
with you are found the true gifts that last. Bless us with

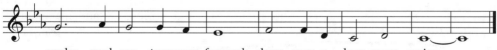

spoke and wa - ters were formed; deep seas o - bey your voice.
life that nev - er shall end, e - ter - nal life with you.

Text: Joseph R. Renville (1779-1846); tr. Philip Frazier (1892-1964)
Music: Traditonal Dakota

LACQUIPARLE

God of the Word

Out of the bab - ble that sur - rounds us, out of the
cha - os that's with - in, where can we go to find our
mean-ing? Is there a place we can be - gin?
God of the Word, now let the Word be spo - ken. Word of our
God, come vis - it us with grace. Rise like a fra - grance,
like a chord of mu - sic, fill - ing all this ho - ly place.

Text and music: Ken Medema (b. 1943)

85

Psalm 1

Round F

Hap-py are they who trust, who trust in the Lord.

Refrain

1 Happy are those
who do not follow the advice of the wicked,
or take the path that sinners tread,
or sit in the seat of scoffers;
2 **but their delight is in the law of the LORD,
and on his law they meditate day and
night.**
3 They are like trees
planted by streams of water,
which yield their fruit in its season,
and their leaves do not wither.
In all that they do, they prosper.

Refrain

4 The wicked are not so,
but are like chaff that the wind drives
away.
5 **Therefore the wicked will not stand in the
judgment,
nor sinners in the congregation of the
righteous;**
6 for the LORD watches over the way of the
righteous,
but the way of the wicked will perish.

Refrain

Refrain: Robert J. Thompson

86

Thy Word

Refrain

Thy Word is a lamp un-to my feet and a light un-to my

Fine

path.   1 When I feel a-fraid,   think I've lost my way,
2 I will not for-get your love for me and yet my

still you're there right be-side me. And noth-ing will I fear as
heart for-ev-er is wan-der-ing.   Je-sus, be my guide and

Text: Amy Grant (b. 1960)
Music: Michael W. Smith (b. 1957)

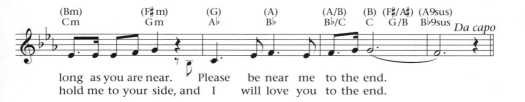

long as you are near. Please be near me to the end.
hold me to your side, and I will love you to the end.

Psalm 119 87

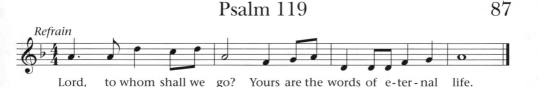

Lord, to whom shall we go? Yours are the words of e-ter-nal life.

Refrain

¹ Happy are those whose way is blameless,
who walk in the law of the LORD.
² **Happy are those who keep his decrees,**
who seek him with their whole heart,
³ **who also do no wrong,**
but walk in his ways.
⁴ You have commanded your precepts
to be kept diligently.
⁵ **O that my ways may be steadfast**
in keeping your statutes!
⁶ Then I shall not be put to shame,
having my eyes fixed on all your
commandments.
⁷ **I will praise you with an upright heart,**
when I learn your righteous ordinances.
⁸ **I will observe your statutes;**
do not utterly forsake me.

Refrain

³³Teach me, O LORD, the way of your
statutes,
and I will observe it to the end.
³⁴**Give me understanding, that I may keep**
your law
and observe it with my whole heart.
³⁵Lead me in the path of your
commandments,
for I delight in it.

³⁶**Turn my heart to your decrees,**
and not to selfish gain.
³⁷Turn my eyes from looking at vanities;
give me life in your ways.
³⁸**Confirm to your servant your promise,**
which is for those who fear you.
³⁹Turn away the disgrace that I dread,
for your ordinances are good.
⁴⁰**See, I have longed for your precepts;**
in your righteousness give me life.

Refrain

¹⁰⁵ Your word is a lamp to my feet
and a light to my path.
¹⁰⁶ **I have sworn an oath and confirmed it,**
to observe your righteous ordinances.
¹⁰⁷ I am severely afflicted;
give me life, O LORD, according to
your word.
¹⁰⁸ **Accept my offerings of praise, O LORD,**
and teach me your ordinances.
¹⁰⁹ I hold my life in my hand continually,
but I do not forget your law.
¹¹⁰ **The wicked have laid a snare for me,**
but I do not stray from your precepts.
¹¹¹ Your decrees are my heritage forever;
they are the joy of my heart.

Refrain

Refrain text: John 6:68
Music: The Iona Community

Music © 1995, WGRG the Iona Community (Scotland), admin. GIA Publications, Inc.

88 Psalm 19: God's Glory Fills the Heavens

1 God's glo - ry fills the heavens with hymns;
2 God's per - fect law re - vives the soul;
3 God's ser - vant may I ev - er be:

the domed sky bears the Mak - er's mark.
its pre - cepts make the sim - ple wise.
this world my joy, that word my guide.

New prais - es sound from day to day
Its just com - mands re - joice the heart;
O cleanse me, Lord, from se - cret sin;

and ech - o through the know - ing dark.
its truth gives light un - to the eyes.
de - liv - er me from self - ish pride.

Text: Carl P. Daw, Jr. (b. 1944)
Music: Franz J. Haydn (1732-1809)

LMD
CREATION

With - out a word their songs roll on;
For - ev - er shall this law en - dure:
Ac - cept my thoughts and words and deeds;

in - to all lands their voic - es run.
un - blem - ished, righ - teous, true, com - plete.
let them find fa - vor in your sight.

And with a cham - pion's strength and grace
No gold was ev - er found so fine,
For you a - lone can make me whole,

from far - thest heaven comes forth the sun.
no hon - ey in the comb more sweet.
O Lord, my ref - uge and my might.

89 Lord, We Hear Your Word with Gladness

1 Lord, we hear your word with glad-ness: you have spo-ken— we re - joice:
2 May we hear with un - der-stand-ing, by your Spir - it taught and led.
3 You have spo-ken; yours the full-ness, ours the wealth of this your Word.

words of love and life and free-dom— help us make their truth our choice!
May the springs of all our be - ing by your liv - ing Word be fed.
Debt-ors, then, as liv-ing let - ters we must make your gos - pel heard!

Now in ho - ly cel - e - bra-tion for your Word we wor - ship you;
May our hearts ac - cept with meek-ness all the grace your light makes known.
By your Spir - it's power trans-form us; shed your sav - ing light a - broad

spo-ken, writ-ten, known in Je - sus, ours to - day to prove a - new.
May o - be-dience mark our foot-steps till we make each word our own.
till our lives by love in ac - tion show our world the truth of God!

Text: Margaret Clarkson (b. 1915)
Music: *Columbian Harmony* (1825)
Text © 1987, Hope Publishing Co.

87 87 D
HOLY MANNA

View the Present Through the Promise

1 View the pres - ent through the prom-ise, Christ will come a-gain.
2 Probe the pres - ent with the prom-ise, Christ will come a-gain.
3 Match the pres - ent to the prom-ise, Christ will come a-gain.

Trust de - spite the deep-ening dark-ness, Christ will come a-gain.
Let your dai - ly ac - tions wit - ness, Christ will come a-gain.
Make this hope your guid - ing prem-ise, Christ will come a-gain.

Lift the world a - bove its griev-ing through your watch-ing and be - liev-ing
Let your lov - ing and your giv-ing and your jus - tice and for - giv-ing
Pat-tern all your cal - cu - lat-ing and the world you are cre - a - ting

in the hope past hope's con-ceiv-ing: Christ will come a - gain.
be a sign to all the liv-ing: Christ will come a - gain.
to the ad - vent you are wait-ing: Christ will come a - gain.

Text: Thomas H. Troeger (b. 1945)
Music: Roy Hopp (b. 1951)

Text © 1994, Oxford University Press, Inc.; music © 1997, Roy Hopp

85 85 88 85
FRANKLIN PARK

91   Awake! Awake and Greet the New Morn

1 A - wake!   A - wake   and   greet   the new   morn,   for
2 To   us,   to   all   in   sor - row and   fear,   Em -
3 In   dark - est night   his com - ing shall   be,   when
4 Re - joice,   re - joice,   take   heart   in   the   night,   though

an - gels her - ald its   dawn-ing.   Sing out   your joy,   for
man - u - el comes a - sing-ing;   his hum - ble song   is
all   the world is   de - spair-ing,   as morn - ing light   so
dark   the win - ter and cheer-less.   The ris - ing sun   shall

soon*   he is   born.   Be - hold!   the child of   our   long - ing.
qui - et and near,   yet   fills   the earth with   its   ring - ing:
qui - et and free,   so   warm   and gen - tle and   car - ing.
crown you with light;   be strong   and lov - ing and   fear - less.

Come as   a   ba - by weak   and poor,   to   bring   all hearts   to -
Mu - sic   to heal   the bro - ken soul   and hymns   of   lov - ing
Then shall the mute break forth   in   song,   the lame   shall leap   in
Love be   our song   and love   our prayer,   and love,   our   end - less

geth - er,   he   o - pens wide   the heav'n - ly   door   and
kind - ness. The thun - der   of   his   an - thems roll   to
won - der,   the weak   be raised   a - bove   the strong,   and
sto - ry.   May God   fill   ev - ery   day   we share,   and

* May be sung during the Christmas season by changing stanza 1, line 3 "soon" to "now."

Text and music: Marty Haugen (b. 1950)   98 98 87 89
© 1983, GIA Publications, Inc.   REJOICE REJOICE

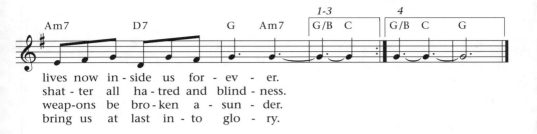

lives now in - side us for - ev - er.
shat - ter all ha - tred and blind - ness.
weap-ons be bro-ken a - sun - der.
bring us at last in - to glo - ry.

He Came Down

92

He came down that we may have hope,* he
came down that we may have hope,* he came down that we may
have hope.* Hal -le - lu - jah for - ev - er - more.

(Why did Christ come?)

* peace, joy, love, life

Text and music: Cameroon traditional; tr. and arr. John Bell (b. 1949)

93 Toda la tierra / All Earth Is Waiting

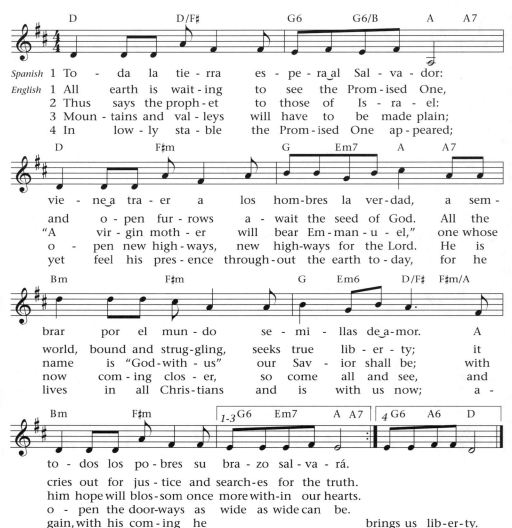

Spanish 1 To - da la tie - rra es - pe - ra al Sal - va - dor:
English 1 All earth is wait - ing to see the Prom - ised One,
2 Thus says the proph - et to those of Is - ra - el:
3 Moun - tains and val - leys will have to be made plain;
4 In low - ly sta - ble the Prom - ised One ap - peared;

vie - ne a tra - er a los hom - bres la ver - dad, a sem -
and o - pen fur - rows a - wait the seed of God. All the
"A vir - gin moth - er will bear Em - man - u - el," one whose
o - pen new high - ways, new high - ways for the Lord. He is
yet feel his pres - ence through - out the earth to - day, for he

brar por el mun - do se - mi - llas de a - mor. A
world, bound and strug - gling, seeks true lib - er - ty; it
name is "God - with - us" our Sav - ior shall be; with
now com - ing clos - er, so come all and see, and
lives in all Chris - tians and is with us now; a -

to - dos los po - bres su bra - zo sal - va - rá.
cries out for jus - tice and search - es for the truth.
him hope will blos - som once more with - in our hearts.
o - pen the door - ways as wide as wide can be.
gain, with his com - ing he brings us lib - er - ty.

2 Dice el profeta al pueblo de Israel:
"Pronto la luz del Mesías brillará.
Dios se acerca a nosotros: su nombre, Emmanuel".
¡Germine la tierra amor y libertad!

3 De nuestra carne se quiso revestir,
pobre y sencillo, de humilde corazón.
Nacerá como entonces, vendrá a compartir
la suerte del hombre, su angustia y su dolor.

4 Él viene siempre. Vivimos de esperar
todos los días la vuelta de Jesús.
¡Contemplad su mirada, su voz escuchad,
dejad que las sombras se llenen de su luz!

Text: Tirso Vaquero; tr. Gertrude C. Suppe (b. 1911)
Music: Alberto Taulé (b. 1932)

11 11 12 12
TAULÉ

Lighting of the Advent Candles

On the First Sunday of Advent
We light this (these) candle(s) as a sign of the coming light of Christ.
In the wilderness prepare the way of the Lord,
make straight in the desert a highway for our God.   —Isaiah 40:3

All sing 93, st. 1

On the Second Sunday of Advent
Repeat from the preceding week and add the following:

The Lord will give you a sign.
A young woman is with child and shall bear a son.
And they shall name him Emmanuel,
which means "God is with us."   —Isaiah 7:14, Matthew 1:23

All sing 93, st. 1-2

On the Third Sunday of Advent
Repeat from the preceding weeks and add the following:

Every valley shall be lifted up
and every mountain and hill be made low;
the uneven ground shall become level,
and the rough places a plain.   —Isaiah 40:4

All sing 93, st. 1-3

On the Fourth Sunday of Advent
Repeat from the preceding weeks and add the following:

Then the glory of the Lord shall be revealed,
and all the people shall see it together,
for the mouth of the Lord has spoken.   —Isaiah 40:5

All sing 93, st. 1-4

On Christmas Eve or Christmas Day
Repeat from the preceding weeks and add the following:

The Word became flesh and lived among us.
And we have seen his glory,
the glory as of a father's only son, full of grace and truth.   —John 1:14

My Soul in Stillness Waits

Refrain

For you, O Lord, my soul in still-ness waits;

tru-ly my hope is in you.

1 O Lord of
2 O Spring of
3 O Root of
4 O Key of

Light, our on-ly hope of glo - ry, your ra-diance
Joy, rain down up-on our spir - its; our thirst-y
Life, im-plant your seed with-in us, and in your
Knowl - edge, guide us in our pil-grim-age; we ev-er

shines in all who look to you. Come, light the
hearts are yearn-ing for your Word. Come, make us
ad - vent draw us all to you, our hope re-
seek, yet un-ful-filled re - main. O - pen to

hearts of all in dark and shad-ow.
whole; be com-fort to our hearts.___
born in dy-ing and in ris-ing.
us the path-way of your peace.___

Text and music: Marty Haugen (b. 1950), based on Psalm 95 and "O" Antiphons

Psalm 40

Refrain — Wait for the Lord, whose day is near.
Wait for the Lord; be strong, take heart!

Refrain

¹ I waited patiently for the LORD;
  he inclined to me and heard my cry.
² He drew me up from the desolate pit,
  out of the miry bog,
and set my feet upon a rock,
  making my steps secure.
³ He put a new song in my mouth,
  a song of praise to our God.
  Many will see and fear,
    and put their trust in the LORD.
⁴ **Happy are those who make**
    the LORD their trust,
  who do not turn to the proud,
    to those who go astray after false gods.
⁵ You have multiplied, O LORD my God,
  your wondrous deeds and your
    thoughts toward us;
  none can compare with you.
Were I to proclaim and tell of them,
  they would be more than can be
    counted.

Refrain

⁶ Sacrifice and offering you do not desire,
  but you have given me an open ear.
Burnt offering and sin offering
  you have not required.
⁷ **Then I said, "Here I am;**
    in the scroll of the book it is written of
    me.
⁸ **I delight to do your will, O my God;**
    your law is within my heart."
⁹ I have told the glad news of deliverance
  in the great congregation;
see, I have not restrained my lips,
  as you know, O LORD.
¹⁰ **I have not hidden your saving help within**
    my heart,
  I have spoken of your faithfulness and
    your salvation;
  I have not concealed your steadfast love
    and your faithfulness
  from the great congregation.

Refrain

Refrain text: The Community of Taizé
Music: Jacques Berthier (1923-1994)

97   Psalm 42

Refrain

As a deer in want of wa-ter, so I long for you, O Lord.

Refrain

¹ As a deer longs for flowing streams,
  so my soul longs for you, O God.
² My soul thirsts for God,
  for the living God.
When shall I come and behold
  the face of God?
³ **My tears have been my food**
  day and night,
while people say to me continually,
"Where is your God?"
⁴ These things I remember,
  as I pour out my soul:
how I went with the throng,
  and led them in procession to the
    house of God,
with glad shouts and songs of thanksgiving,
  a multitude keeping festival.
⁵ Why are you cast down, O my soul,
  and why are you disquieted within me?
Hope in God; for I shall again praise him,
  my help ⁶and my God.

Refrain

⁸ By day the LORD commands his steadfast
  love,
  and at night his song is with me,
  a prayer to the God of my life.
⁹ **I say to God, my rock,**
  "Why have you forgotten me?
Why must I walk about mournfully
  because the enemy oppresses me?"

⁴³:³ O send out your light and your
  truth;
  let them lead me;
let them bring me to your holy hill
  and to your dwelling.
⁴ **Then I will go to the altar of God,**
  to God my exceeding joy;
and I will praise you with the harp
  O God, my God.
⁵ Why are you cast down, O my soul,
  and why are you disquieted within me?
Hope in God; for I shall again praise him,
  my help and my God.

Refrain

Refrain text: *Psalter Hymnal* (1987)
Music: Louis Bourgeois (c. 1510 - c. 1561); harm. Johann Crüger (1598-1662)
Text © 1987, CRC Publications

GENEVAN 42

Make Way

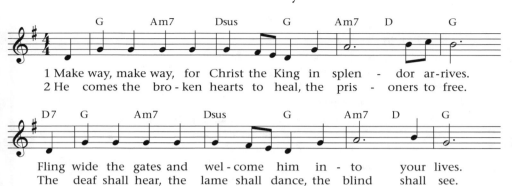

1 Make way, make way, for Christ the King in splen - dor ar-rives.
2 He comes the bro - ken hearts to heal, the pris - oners to free.

Fling wide the gates and wel - come him in - to your lives.
The deaf shall hear, the lame shall dance, the blind shall see.

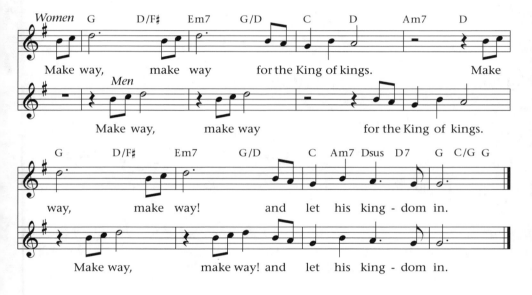

Women
Make way, make way for the King of kings. Make

Men
Make way, make way for the King of kings.

way, make way! and let his king - dom in.

Make way, make way! and let his king - dom in.

Text and music: Graham Kendrick (b. 1950)

99 — Advent Prayer

Lord Jesus Christ,
your world awaits you.
In the longing of the persecuted for justice;
in the longing of the poor for prosperity;
in the longing of the privileged for riches greater than wealth;
in the longing of our hearts for a better life;
and in the song of your Church, expectation is ever present.
O come, Lord, desire behind our greatest needs.
O come, Lord, liberator of humanity.
O come, Lord, O come, Immanuel.
Amen.

100 — Psalm 80

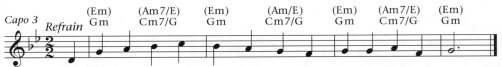

Re-store us, Lord, and show your face, and then we shall be saved.

Refrain

¹ Give ear, O Shepherd of Israel,
  you who lead Joseph like a flock!
You who are enthroned upon the
    cherubim, shine forth
² before Ephraim and Benjamin and
    Manasseh.
Stir up your might,
    and come to save us!

Refrain

⁴ O Lord God of hosts,
    how long will you be angry with your
    people's prayers?

⁵ You have fed them with the bread of tears,
    and given them tears to drink in full
    measure.
⁶ You make us the scorn of our neighbors;
    our enemies laugh among themselves.

Refrain

¹⁷ But let your hand be upon the one at
    your right hand,
    the one whom you made strong for
    yourself.
¹⁸ Then we will never turn back from you;
    give us life, and we will call on your
    name.

Refrain

Refrain text: Bert Polman (b. 1945)
Music: French folk tune (16th cent.)

Text © 2001, CRC Publications

UNE JEUNE PUCELLE

God of Justice Ever Flowing

1 God of jus-tice ev-er flow-ing, right-teous-ness be-yond de-gree,
2 Com-ing as a ti-ny ba-by, giv-ing up your power and might,
3 Some may cel-e-brate with pres-ents; some may greet the day through tears.

breath of mer-cy ev-er blow-ing through our world to set us free:
so in ten-der-ness we may be moved to jus-tice, love and light:
Still in all, your ho-ly pres-ence glad-dens hearts, casts out our fears.

you have lift-ed up the hum-ble and the thrones of power cast down,
help us see in ev-ery child___ that the Christ child dwells with-in,
Teach us how to live more sim-ply, that we all may sim-ply live,

caused the proud of heart to stum-ble, sent a child to wear a crown.
calls us to be re-con-cil-ed, leads to jus-tice, frees from sin.
car-ing for the poor and lone-ly, in Christ's name our love to give.

Lenten Stanzas

1 God of justice everflowing, righteousness beyond degree,
   breath of mercy ever blowing through our world to set us free:
   let your justice roll like waters, goodness like the living stream,
   so that we, your sons and daughters, catch the vision, dream the dream.

2 Scales are still unjustly weighted, children sold to make new shoes,
   while our appetites are sated and we turn from troubling news.
   Cleanse our hearts, give us compassion to respond in Jesus' name,
   offering love through prayer and action, peace with justice to proclaim.

3 Some may live in ease and pleasure, others, suffering, slave away.
   Some have luxury and treasure, others struggle day to day.
   Teach us how to live more simply, that we all may simply live,
   caring for the poor yet worthy, in Christ's name our love to give.

Text: Kathleen R. Moore (20th cent.)
Music: *Columbian Harmony* (1825)
See 89 for harmony.

87 87 D
HOLY MANNA

102

Song of Mary /
My Soul Proclaims with Wonder

Text: Carl P. Daw, Jr. (b. 1944), based on Luke 1:46-55
Music: German; desc. Roy Hopp (b. 1951)

76 76 D
ES FLOG EIN KLEINS WALDVOGELEIN

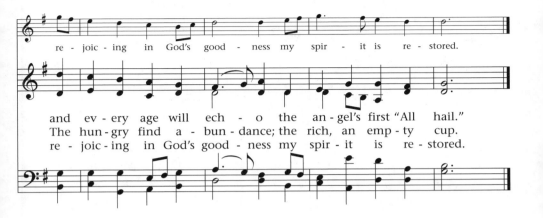

re - joic - ing in God's good - ness my spir - it is re - stored.

and ev - ery age will ech - o the an - gel's first "All hail."
The hun - gry find a - bun - dance; the rich, an emp - ty cup.
re - joic - ing in God's good - ness my spir - it is re - stored.

Come, Lord Jesus 103

1 Come, Lord Je - sus. Come, Lord Je - sus.
2 Come, O Prince of Peace. Come, O Prince of Peace.
3 Come, Im - man - u - el. Come, Im - man - u - el.

Come, Lord Je - sus;
Come, O Prince of Peace; Come, and be born in our hearts.
Come, Im - man - u - el;

Text and music: Carey Landry (b. 1955)

104

Song of Zechariah /
Blessed Be the God of Israel

Descant

3 My child, as proph-et of the Lord you will pre-pare the way,

1 Blessed be the God of Is - ra - el who comes to set us free
2 With prom-ised mer - cy will God still the cov - e - nant re - call,
3 My child, as proph-et of the Lord you will pre-pare the way,

to tell God's peo - ple they are saved from sin's e - ter - nal sway.

and rais - es up new hope for us: a Branch from Da-vid's tree.
the oath once sworn to A - bra - ham, from foes to save us all,
to tell God's peo - ple they are saved from sin's e - ter - nal sway.

Then shall God's mer - cy from on high shine forth and nev - er cease

So have the proph-ets long de-clared that with a might-y arm
that we might wor-ship with-out fear and of - fer lives of praise,
Then shall God's mer - cy from on high shine forth and nev - er cease

Text: Carl P. Daw, Jr. (b.1944), based on the Song of Zechariah, Luke 1:68-79
Music: English folk tune; adapt. and harm. Ralph Vaughan Williams (1872-1958);
 desc. Thomas Armstrong (1898-1994)

CMD
FOREST GREEN

God would turn back our en - e - mies and all who wish us harm.
in ho - li - ness and righ - teous-ness to serve God all our days.
to drive a - way the gloom of death and lead us in - to peace.

Prepare the Way

105

Round
Capo 1

Pre - pare the way of the Lord. Pre-pare the way of the Lord, and

all peo-ple will see the sal - va - tion of our God. Pre -

Text: Isaiah 40:3; 52:10
Music: Jacques Berthier (1923-1994)

106 Soon and Very Soon

1,4 Soon and ver-y soon, we are going to see the King!
2 No more cry-ing there— we are going to see the King!
3 No more dy-ing there— we are going to see the King!

Soon and ver-y soon, we are going to see the King!
No more cry-ing there— we are going to see the King!
No more dy-ing there— we are going to see the King!

Soon and ver-y soon, we are going to see the King! Hal-le-
No more cry-ing there— we are going to see the King! Hal-le-
No more dy-ing there— we are going to see the King! Hal-le-

lu-jah! Hal-le-lu-jah! We're going to see the King!

Text and music: Andraé Crouch (b. 1947)

© 1976, Bud John Songs, Inc./Crouch Music, admin. EMI Christian Music Publishing

SOON AND VERY SOON

Mary Had a Baby

1 Mar - y had a ba - by, my Lord. Mar - y had a
2 What did — she name him, my Lord? What did — she
3 She named him King Je - sus, my Lord. She named — him King
4 Where was — he born, — my Lord? Where was — he
5 Born in — a man - ger, my Lord. Born in — a

ba - by, my Lord. Mar - y had a ba - by, Mar - y had a
name him, my Lord? What did — she name him, what did — she
Je - sus, my Lord. She named him King Je - sus, she named him King
born, — my Lord? Where was — he born, — where was — he
man - ger, my Lord. Born in — a man - ger, born in — a

ba - by, Mar - y had a ba - by, my Lord.
name him, what did — she name him, my Lord?
Je - sus, she named — him King Je - sus, my Lord.
born, — where was — he born, — my Lord?
man - ger, born in — a man - ger, my Lord.

Text and music: African-American spiritual; arr. Kenneth L. Fenton (b. 1938)

108   Jesus, Jesus, Oh, What a Wonderful Child

Text and music: African-American spiritual; harm. Jeffrey Radford (b. 1953)

Harm. © 1992, Pilgrim Press

WONDERFUL CHILD

This Is Your God /
Meekness and Majesty

1 Meek-ness and maj-es-ty, man-hood and De-i-ty
2 Fa-ther's pure ra-di-ance, per-fect in in-no-cence,
3 Wis-dom un-search-a-ble, God the in-vis-i-ble,

in per-fect har-mo-ny, the Man who is God.
yet learns o-be-di-ence to death on a cross,
Love in-de-struct-i-ble in frail-ty ap-pears.

Lord of e-ter-ni-ty dwells in hu-man-i-ty,
suf-fering to give us life, con-quering through sac-ri-fice,
Lord of in-fin-i-ty, stoop-ing so ten-der-ly,

kneels in hu-mil-i-ty and wash-es our feet.
and, as they cru-ci-fy, prays, "Fa-ther, for-give."
lifts our hu-man-i-ty to the heights of his throne.

Refrain

Oh, what a mys-ter-y— meek-ness and maj-es-ty;

bow down and wor-ship, for

this is your God.

Text and music: Graham Kendrick (b. 1950)

66 65 66 65 with refrain
MEEKNESS AND MAJESTY

110 Hitsuji Wa / Sheep Fast Asleep

Japanese 1 Hi - tsu - ji wa ne - mu - re ri, ku - sa - no to - ko ni,
English 1 Sheep fast a - sleep, there on a hill, grass for their bed; all is still.
2 Star in the sky, shin - ing so bright, si - lent and pure, won - drous light!
3 Glo - ry to God! Glo - ry on high! Sing you "No - el!" Day is nigh!

sa - e - yu - ku fu - yu no yo shi - mo mo mi - e - tsu.
Cold win - ter night, the frost ap - pears; shep - herds keep watch by their fire.
What tid - ings brings it Is - ra - el? Can we new hope in it find?
All you who dwell on earth be - low, peace be to you, and good - will.

Ha - ru - ka ni hi - bi - ku wa ka - ze - ka, mi - zu ka,
Soft there a sound, far, far a - way. Is it the stream? Winds at play?
Good news it brings! "Fear not, I pray! Born is God's Son, born to - day!
Come, let us go to Beth - le - hem; fol - low the star, seek - ing him.

Text: Genzo Miwa (20th cent.), Japanese; tr. John Moss (b. 1925)
Music: Chûgoro Torii (1898-1986)

87 87 87 86
KORIN

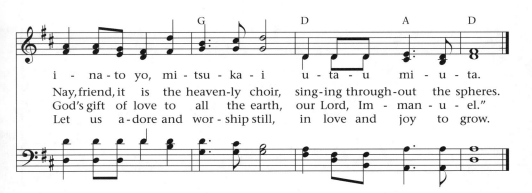

i - na - to yo, mi - tsu - ka - i   u - ta - u   mi - u - ta.
Nay, friend, it is the heaven-ly choir, sing-ing through-out the spheres.
God's gift of love to all the earth, our Lord, Im - man - u - el."
Let us a - dore and wor - ship still, in love and joy to grow.

2 * Mahiru ni otoranu ku<u>shi</u>ki hikari,
    misora no kanata ni terikaka<u>ya</u> ku.
    Sukui wo motarasu Ka<u>mi</u> no miko no
    umareshi yorokobi tsuguru hoshi ka.

3 Ame ni wa misakae Ka<u>mi</u> ni areya,
   tsuchi ni wa odayaka hito ni a<u>re</u> to
   mukashi no shirabe wo <u>ima</u> ni kaeshi,
   utaeya, tomora yo, koemo takaku.

Each vowel is a separate syllable. Sing underlined syllables to two notes.

Gloria   111

Latin   Glo - ri-a,   glo - ri-a,   glo - ri-a   in ex-cel-sis De - o.

Text and music: Traditional, from Luke 2:14

112 Psalm 98: Sing a New Song to the Lord

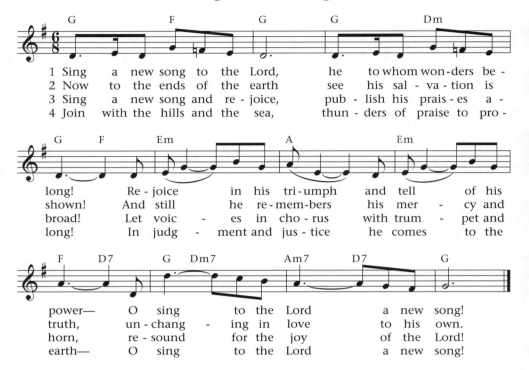

1 Sing a new song to the Lord, he to whom wonders be-
2 Now to the ends of the earth see his salvation is
3 Sing a new song and rejoice, publish his praises a-
4 Join with the hills and the sea, thunders of praise to pro-

long! Rejoice in his triumph and tell of his
shown! And still he remembers his mercy and
broad! Let voices in chorus with trumpet and
long! In judgment and justice he comes to the

power— O sing to the Lord a new song!
truth, unchanging in love to his own.
horn, resound for the joy of the Lord!
earth— O sing to the Lord a new song!

Text: Psalm 98; vers. Timothy Dudley-Smith (b. 1926)
Music: David G. Wilson (b. 1940)

77 11 8
ONSLOW SQUARE

Text © 1973, Hope Publishing Co.; music © 1973, Jubilate Hymns, Ltd., admin. Hope Publishing Co.

113 Psalm 97: Blessed Be the Lord

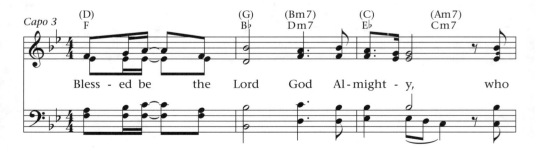

Bless - ed be the Lord God Al-might-y, who

Refrain: Bob Fitts (b. 1955)

LORD GOD ALMIGHTY

© 1984, Scripture in Song (a div. of Integrity Music, Inc.)

was, and is and is to come. Bless - ed be the
Lord God Al-might - y, who reigns for-ev - er - more.

Refrain

1 The LORD is king! Let the earth rejoice;
  let the many coastlands be glad!
2 Clouds and thick darkness are all around him;
  righteousness and justice are the foundation of his throne.
3 Fire goes before him,
  and consumes his adversaries on every side.
4 His lightnings light up the world;
  the earth sees and trembles.
5 The mountains melt like wax before the LORD,
  before the Lord of all the earth.
6 **The heavens proclaim his righteousness;**
  and all the peoples behold his glory.

Refrain

7 All worshipers of images are put to shame,
  those who make their boast in worthless idols;
  all gods bow down before him.
8 Zion hears and is glad,
  and the towns of Judah rejoice,
  because of your judgments, O God.
9 **For you, O LORD, are most high over all**
  the earth;
  you are exalted far above all gods.

10 The LORD loves those who hate evil;
  he guards the lives of his faithful;
  he rescues them from the hand of the wicked.
11 Light dawns for the righteous,
  and joy for the upright in heart.
12 **Rejoice in the LORD, O you righteous,**
  and give thanks to his holy name!

Refrain

114 Jesus, Name Above All Names

1 Je - sus, name a-bove all names, beau-ti-ful
2 Praise him, Lord a-bove all lords, King a-bove

Sav - ior, glo - ri - ous Lord. Em-
all kings, God's on - ly Son, the

man - u - el, God__ is with us, bless - ed Re -
Prince of Peace, who by his Spir - it comes to live

deem - er, Liv - ing Word.
in us, Mas - ter and Friend.

Text and music: Naida Hearn (1944-2001)

HEARN

115 Gloria, Gloria

Round

Latin Glo - ri - a, glo - ri - a, in ex - cel - sis De - o!

Glo - ri - a, glo - ri - a, al - le - lu - ia, al - le - lu - ia!

Text: Luke 2:14
Music: Jacques Berthier (1923-1994)

Gloria / Glory

Spanish Glo - ria, glo - ria, glo - ria en las al - tu - ras a Dios,
English Glo - ry, glo - ry, glo - ry, glo - ry be to God on high,

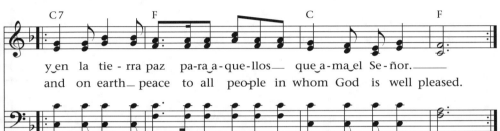

y en la tie - rra paz pa - ra a - que - llos__ que a - ma el Se - ñor.__
and on earth__ peace to all peo - ple in whom God is well pleased.

Text: Luke 2:14
Music: Pablo Sosa (b. 1947), Argentina

© 1989, Pablo Sosa, admin. OCP Publications

CUEQUITA

Emmanuel, Emmanuel 117

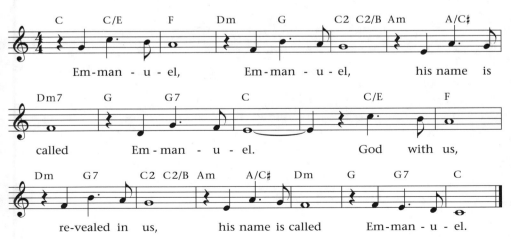

Em - man - u - el, Em - man - u - el, his name is

called Em - man - u - el. God with us,

re - vealed in us, his name is called Em - man - u - el.

Text and music: Bob McGee (b.1944)

© 1976, C.A. Music (a div. of C.A. Records, Inc.), admin. Music Services

88 78
EMMANUEL

118 Los magos que llegaron a Belén /
The Magi Went to Bethl'hem Long Ago

Spanish Los ma-gos que lle-ga-ron a Be-lén a nun-
English The ma-gi went to Beth-l'hem long a-go and an-

cia-ron la lle-ga-da del Me-sí-as y no-so-tros, con a-le-
nounced the prom-ised birth of the Mes-si-ah. And with joy we join in the

grí-a, la a-nun-cia-mos hoy tam-bién.
tell-ing of the news a-gain to-day.

1 De tie-rra le-ja-na ve-ni-mos a
2 Al re-cién na-ci-do que es Rey de los
1 From a dis-tant home the Sav-ior we come
2 Glow-ing gold, I bring the new-born babe so

ver-te, nos sir-ve de guí-a la es-tre-lla de O-rien-te.
re-yes, o-ro le re-ga-lo pa-ra or-nar sus sie-nes.
seek-ing, us-ing as our guide the stars so bright-ly beam-ing.
ho-ly, to-ken of his power to reign a-bove in glo-ry.

Text and music: Traditional Puerto Rican carol; tr. George K. Evans (b. 1917)

12 12 with refrain
ISLA DEL ENCANTO

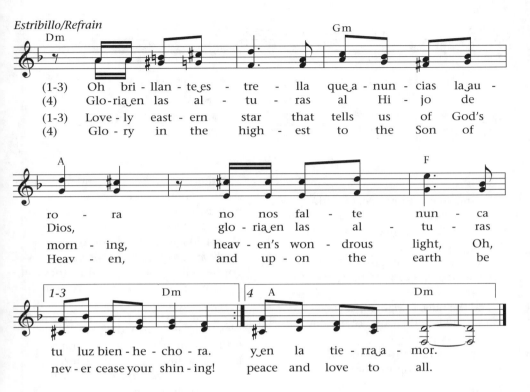

Estribillo/Refrain

(1-3) Oh bri - llan - te es - tre - lla que a - nun - cias la au -
(4) Glo - ria en las al - tu - ras al Hi - jo de
(1-3) Love - ly east - ern star that tells us of God's
(4) Glo - ry in the high - est to the Son of

ro - ra no nos fal - te nun - ca
Dios, glo - ria en las al - tu - ras
morn - ing, heav - en's won - drous light, Oh,
Heav - en, and up - on the earth be

1-3
tu luz bien - he - cho - ra.
nev - er cease your shin - ing!

4
y en la tie - rra a - mor.
peace and love to all.

3 Como es Dios el Niño le regalo incienso,
  perfume con alma que sube hasta el cielo
  Estribillo

4 Al Niño del cielo que bajó a la tierra,
  le regalo mirra que inspira tristeza.
  Estribillo

3 Frankincense I bring the child of God's
  own choosing, token of our prayers
  to heaven ever rising. *Refrain*

4 Bitter myrrh have I to give the infant
  Jesus, token of the pain that he will bear
  to save us. *Refrain*

Epiphany Prayer 119

Eternal God,
by a star you led magi to the worship of your Son.
Guide the nations of the earth by your light,
that the whole world may see your glory;
through Jesus Christ our Lord,
who lives and reigns with you and the Holy Spirit,
one God, now and forever.
Amen.

120

Psalm 72

Refrain

Hail to the Lord's a-noint-ed, great Da-vid's great-er son!

Refrain

1 Give the king your justice, O God,
 and your righteousness to a king's son.
2 May he judge your people with
 righteousness,
 and your poor with justice.
3 **May the mountains yield prosperity for
 the people,
 and the hills, in righteousness.**
4 May he defend the cause of the poor of
 the people,
 give deliverance to the needy,
 and crush the oppressor.

Refrain

5 May he live while the sun endures,
 and as long as the moon, throughout
 all generations.
6 **May he be like rain that falls on the mown
 grass,
 like showers that water the earth.**
7 In his days may righteousness flourish
 and peace abound, until the moon is
 no more.

Refrain

10 May the kings of Tarshish and of the isles
 render him tribute,
 may the kings of Sheba and Seba
 bring gifts.
11 **May all kings fall down before him,
 all nations give him service.**
12 For he delivers the needy when they call,
 the poor and those who have no helper.

Refrain

18 Blessed be the LORD, the God of Israel,
 who alone does wondrous things.
19 Blessed be his glorious name forever;
 may his glory fill the whole earth.
 Amen and Amen.

Refrain

Refrain text: James Montgomery (1771-1854)
Music: German; see also 102

ES FLOG EIN KLEINS WALDVOGELEIN

Jesus the Lord Said, "I Am the Bread"

1 Je - sus the Lord said, "I am the bread; the bread of life for the world am I. The bread of life for the world am I; the bread of life for the world am I." Je - sus the Lord said, "I am the bread; the bread of life for the world am I."

2 Je - sus the Lord said, "I am the light; the one true light of the world am I. The one true light of the world am I; the one true light of the world am I." Je - sus the Lord said, "I am the light; the one true light of the world am I."

3 Je - sus the Lord said, "I am the door; the way and the door for the sheep am I. The way and the door for the sheep am I; the way and the door for the sheep am I." Je - sus the Lord said, "I am the door; the way and the door for the sheep am I."

4 Jesus the Lord said, "I am the shepherd;
   the one good shepherd of the sheep am I. . . ."

5 Jesus the Lord said, "I am the life;
   the resurrection and the life am I. . . ."

6 Jesus the Lord said, "I am the way;
   the way of truth and life am I. . . ."

7 Jesus the Lord said, "I am the vine;
   the vine that feeds every branch am I. . . ."

Text: st. 1-5, Anonymous Urdu, tr. C. Dermott Monahan (1906-1957); st. 6-7, Bert Polman (b. 1945); based on "I Am" passages in the Gospel of John
Music: Urdu melody

YISU NE KAHA

Text: st. 1-5 © 1969, Christian Conference of Asia; st. 6-7 © 2001, CRC Publications

122 Blest Are They

Text: David Haas (b. 1957), based on Matthew 5:3-12
Music: David Haas; desc. Michael Joncas (b. 1951)

BLEST ARE THEY

Bring Forth the Kingdom

123

1 You are— salt for the earth, O peo-ple: salt for the king-dom of God!
2 You are a light on a hill, O peo-ple: light for the cit - y of God!
3 You are a seed of the Word, O peo-ple: live for the king-dom of God!

Share the fla-vor of life, O peo-ple: life in the king-dom of God!
Shine so ho-ly and bright, O peo-ple: shine for the king-dom of God!
Seeds of mer-cy and seeds of jus-tice, grow in the king-dom of God!

Descants

Bring forth the king - dom of mer - cy; pray for the king - dom of peace;

Bring forth the king-dom of mer-cy; pray for the king-dom of peace;

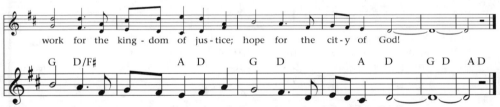

work for the king - dom of jus-tice; hope for the cit-y of God!

work for the king-dom of jus-tice; hope for the cit-y of God!

Text and music: Marty Haugen (b. 1950), based on Matthew 5:13-16

124   Jesus Heard with Deep Compassion

1 Je - sus heard with deep com - pas - sion pleas for heal - ing,
2 Je - sus touched the lives of out - casts, weak or sin - ful,
3 Je - sus, Lord, our true ex - am - ple, you have shown how

cries of pain; cured the lame and cleansed the lep - er, gave the
scorned or poor; gave them self - re - spect and cour - age, trust and
we must live. Teach us how to share with oth - ers ev - ery -

blind their sight a - gain. At his voice, tor - ment - ing
faith and hope se - cure. Tru - ly hear - ing, tru - ly
thing we have to give. Let our days be spent in

spir - its fled a mad - man's tor - tured mind; clothed and
see - ing deep with - in each trou - bled soul, Je - sus
serv - ice; bring us by your grace to know heal - ing

Text: Joy F. Patterson (b. 1931)
Music: J. Leavitt's *Christian Lyre* (1830); harm. Ralph Vaughan Williams (1872-1958)

87 87 D
PLEADING SAVIOR

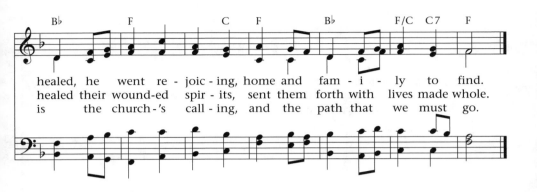

healed, he went re - joic - ing, home and fam - i - ly to find.
healed their wound-ed spir - its, sent them forth with lives made whole.
is the church -'s call - ing, and the path that we must go.

Take Us As We Are, O God   125

1 Take us as we are, O God, and claim us as your own. As
2 Bless us for your ser - vice, Lord; no pow - er we de - vise will
3 Break us o - pen to dis - close how bro - ken-ness can heal, where-
4 Give us to the world you love as light and salt and yeast, that

once you chose to tell your love in hu - man flesh and bone, so
ev - er give us strength e - nough or make us tru - ly wise, yet
ev - er bro - ken loaves suf - fice to give a crowd a meal and
we may nour - ish in your name the last, the lost, the least, un -

let our lives be used to make your sav - ing pur - pose known.
by your prom - ise we can know the peace your grace sup - plies.
graves break o - pen to re - lease new life from death's dread seal.
til at length you call us all to your un - end - ing feast.

Text: Carl P. Daw, Jr. (b. 1944)
Music: Alfred V. Fedak (b. 1953)

76 86 86
ENDLESS FEAST

126 We Have Come at Christ's Own Bidding

1 We have come at Christ's own bid-ding to this high and
2 Light breaks in up-on our dark-ness; splen-dor bathes the
3 Strength-ened by this glimpse of glo-ry, fear-ful lest our

ho - ly place, where we wait with hope and long-ing
flesh-joined Word; Mos-es and E-li-jah mar-vel
faith de - cline, we like Pe-ter find it tempt-ing

for some to - ken of God's grace. Here we pray for
as the heaven-ly voice is heard. Eyes and hearts be-
to re-main and build a shrine. But true wor - ship

new as-sur-ance that our faith is not in vain, search-ing
hold with won-der how the Law and Pro-phets meet: Christ, with
gives us cour-age to pro-claim what we pro-fess, that our

Text: Carl P. Daw, Jr. (b. 1944)
Music: Cyril V. Taylor (1907-1981)
Alternate tune: HOLY MANNA, 101

87 87 D
ABBOT'S LEIGH

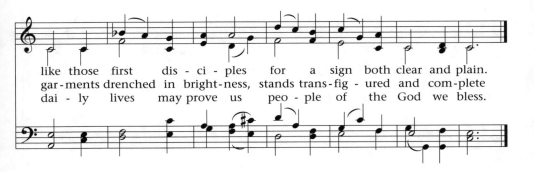

like those first dis - ci - ples for a sign both clear and plain.
gar - ments drenched in bright-ness, stands trans-fig - ured and com-plete
dai - ly lives may prove us peo - ple of the God we bless.

Psalm 29

127

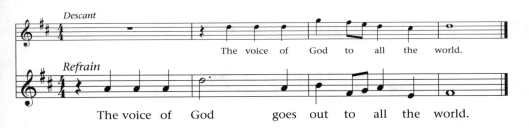

Descant

The voice of God to all the world.

Refrain

The voice of God goes out to all the world.

Refrain

¹ Ascribe to the LORD, O heavenly beings,
   ascribe to the LORD glory and strength.
² **Ascribe to the LORD the glory of his name;**
   worship the LORD in holy splendor.

Refrain

³ The voice of the LORD is over the waters;
   the God of glory thunders,
   the LORD, over mighty waters.
⁴ **The voice of the LORD is powerful;**
   the voice of the LORD is full of majesty.
⁵ The voice of the LORD breaks the cedars;
   the LORD breaks the cedars of Lebanon.
⁶ **He makes Lebanon skip like a calf,**
   and Sir'i-on like a young wild ox.

⁷ The voice of the LORD flashes forth flames
   of fire.
⁸ The voice of the LORD shakes the
   wilderness;
   the LORD shakes the wilderness of
   Kadesh.

⁹ The voice of the LORD causes the oaks to
   whirl,
   and strips the forest bare;
   and in his temple all say, "Glory!"

Refrain

¹⁰ The LORD sits enthroned over the flood;
   the LORD sits enthroned as king forever.
¹¹ **May the LORD give strength to his people!**
   May the LORD bless his people with
   peace!

Refrain

Refrain text: Luke Connaughton (1919-1979)
Music: Walter Greatorex (1879-1949); desc. Randall De Bruyn (b. 1947)
Text © 1972, Mayhew McCrimmon; music by permission of Oxford University Press; desc. © 1983, OCP Publications

WOODLANDS

128

Shine, Jesus, Shine

Text and music: Graham Kendrick (b. 1950)
© 1987, Make Way Music, admin. Music Services

9 9 10 10 3 3 and refrain
SHINE, JESUS, SHINE

Throughout These Lenten Days and Nights 129

May be sung in canon

1 Through-out these Lent - en days and nights we turn to walk the
2 The pil - grim Christ, the Lamb of God, who found in weak-ness
3 We bear the si - lence, cross and pain of hu - man bur - dens,
4 And though the road is hard and steep, the Spir - it ev - er

in - ward way, where, meet - ing Christ, our guide and light, we
great - er power, em - brac - es us, though lost and flawed, and
hu - man strife, while sis - ters, bro - thers help sus - tain our
calls us on through Cal - vary's dy - ing, dark and deep, un -

for canon only

live in hope till Eas - ter day. (till Eas - ter day.)
leads us to his ris - ing hour. (his ris - ing hour.)
cou - rage till the feast of life. (the feast of life.)
til we see the com - ing dawn. (the com - ing dawn.)

5   So let us choose the path of one
    who wore for us the crown of thorn,
    and slept in death that we might wake
    to life on Resurrection Morn!

6   Rejoice, O sons and daughters! Sing
    and shout hosannas! Raise the strain!
    For Christ, whose death Good Friday brings,
    on Easter day will live again!

Text: James Gertmenian (b. 1947)
Music: Thomas Tallis (1505-1585)

Text © 1993, Hope Publishing Co.

LM
TALLIS CANON

130 I Want Jesus to Walk with Me

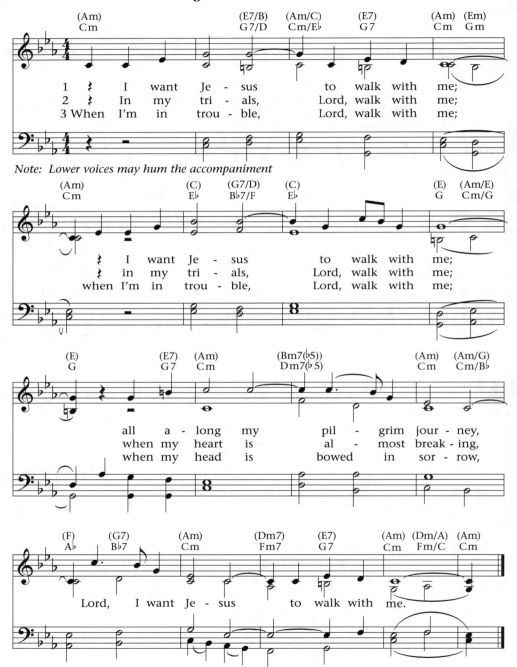

Note: Lower voices may hum the accompaniment

1 I want Je - sus to walk with me;
2 In my tri - als, Lord, walk with me;
3 When I'm in trou - ble, Lord, walk with me;

I want Je - sus to walk with me;
in my tri - als, Lord, walk with me;
when I'm in trou - ble, Lord, walk with me;

all a - long my pil - grim jour - ney,
when my heart is al - most break - ing,
when my head is bowed in sor - row,

Lord, I want Je - sus to walk with me.

Text and music: African-American spiritual; arr. J. Jefferson Cleveland (1937-1986), Verolga Nix (b. 1933)

Arr. © 1981, Abingdon Press, admin. The Copyright Company

SOJOURNER

Psalm 31

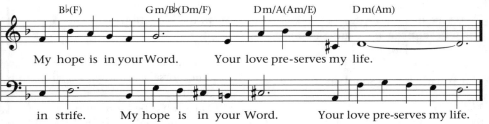

Refrain

¹ In you, O Lord, I seek refuge;
 do not let me ever be put to shame;
 in your righteousness deliver me.
² **Incline your ear to me;**
 rescue me speedily.
Be a rock of refuge for me,
 a strong fortress to save me.

³ You are indeed my rock and my fortress;
 for your name's sake lead me and guide
 me,
⁴ take me out of the net that is hidden for me,
 for you are my refuge.
⁵ **Into your hand I commit my spirit;**
 you have redeemed me, O Lord,
 faithful God.

Refrain

⁹ Be gracious to me, O Lord, for I am in
 distress;
 my eye wastes away from grief,
 my soul and body also.

¹⁰ **For my life is spent with sorrow,**
 and my years with sighing;
my strength fails because of my misery,
 and my bones waste away.

¹¹ I am the scorn of all my adversaries,
 a horror to my neighbors,
 an object of dread to my acquaintances;
 those who see me in the street flee
  from me.
¹² **I have passed out of mind like one who is dead;**
 I have become like a broken vessel.
¹³ For I hear the whispering of many—
 terror all around!—
 as they scheme together against me,
 as they plot to take my life.

¹⁴ **But I trust in you, O Lord;**
 I say, "You are my God."
¹⁵ **My times are in your hand;**
 deliver me from the hand of my
  enemies and persecutors.
¹⁶ Let your face shine upon your servant;
 save me in your steadfast love.

Refrain

Refrain: AnnaMae Meyer Bush (b. 1947); arr. Kathleen Hart Brumm (b. 1958)

MARGARET

132   Psalm 71

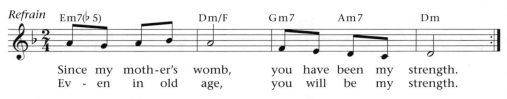

Refrain

Since my moth-er's womb, you have been my strength.
Ev - en in old age, you will be my strength.

Refrain

¹ In you, O LORD, I take refuge;
    let me never be put to shame.
² In your righteousness deliver me and
    rescue me;
    incline your ear to me and save me.
³ Be to me a rock of refuge,
    a strong fortress, to save me,
    for you are my rock and my fortress.

Refrain

⁴ Rescue me, O my God, from the hand of
    the wicked,
    from the grasp of the unjust and cruel.
⁵ For you, O Lord, are my hope,
    my trust, O LORD, from my youth.

⁶ Upon you I have leaned from my birth;
    it was you who took me from my
    mother's womb.
My praise is continually of you.

Refrain

⁹ Do not cast me off in the time of old age;
    do not forsake me when my strength is
    spent.
¹²O God, do not be far from me;
    O my God, make haste to help me!
¹⁴But I will hope continually,
    and will praise you yet more and more.

Refrain

Refrain: Michael Guimont

© 1995, GIA Publications, Inc.

133   Mantos y palmas / Filled with Excitement

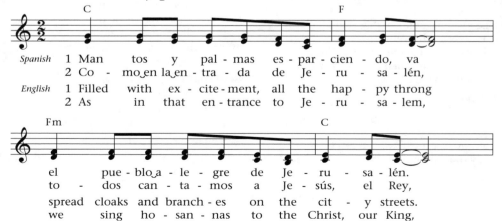

Spanish
1 Man - tos y pal - mas es - par - cien - do, va
2 Co - mo_en la_en - tra - da de Je - ru - sa - lén,

English
1 Filled with ex - cite - ment, all the hap - py throng
2 As in that en - trance to Je - ru - sa - lem,

el pue - blo_a - le - gre de Je - ru - sa - lén.
to - dos can - ta - mos a Je - sús, el Rey,
spread cloaks and branch - es on the cit - y streets.
we sing ho - san - nas to the Christ, our King,

Text: Rubén Ruiz Avila (20th cent.); Eng. tr. Gertrude C. Suppe (b. 1911)
Music: Rubén Ruiz Avila; arr. Alvin Schutmaat (1921-1988)

10 10 10 11 with refrain
HOSANNA

© 1972, 1979, 1989, The United Methodist Publishing House, admin. The Copyright Company

A New Commandment

134

A new com-mand-ment I give un-to you, that you love one an-oth-er as I have loved you, that you love one an-oth-er as I have loved you. By this shall all know that you are my dis-ci-ples, if you have love one for an-oth-er; by this shall all know that you are my dis-

Text: John 13:34-35
Music: Anonymous

NEW COMMANDMENT

ci - ples: if you have love one for an - oth - er.

Friends in Faith

135

1 Friends in faith who fol - low Je - sus, hear the
2 Friends who strive to fol - low Je - sus, walk the
3 Friends who dare to fol - low Je - sus, trust and
4 Firm in faith, now fol - low Je - sus; live the

mes - sage of the cross: World - ly wis - dom
way that Je - sus trod: Spir - it - filled, in
pray through dark - est night: Christ has con - quered
gos - pel you have heard: Be good news to

now is fol - ly; world - ly rich - es count as loss.
hu - man weak - ness, cast your cares up - on our God.
death and e - vil; Christ is joy and life and light.
all who know you, lov - ing do - ers of the Word.

Text: Delores Dufner (b. 1939)
Music: W. Walker's *Southern Harmony* (1835)

55 55 55 54
RESTORATION

136   We Have Been Told

Text and music: David Haas (b. 1957)

© 1983, GIA Publications, Inc.

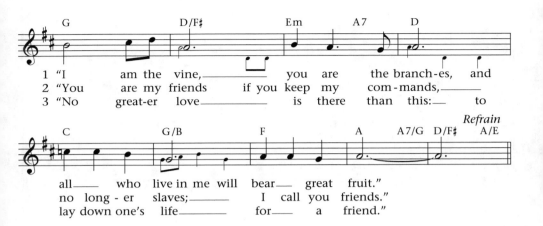

G   D/F♯   Em   A7   D

1 "I   am the vine,_____ you are   the branch-es, and
2 "You   are my friends if you keep my com-mands,_____
3 "No   great-er love_____ is there than this:—   to

Refrain

C   G/B   F   A   A7/G   D/F♯   A/E

all____ who live in me will bear__ great fruit."
no long - er slaves;_____ I   call you friends."
lay down one's life_____ for__   a   friend."

God Is Love 137

A7   D   Bm   Em   A   D   D7   G   A   A7   D   Em7

Be - lov-ed, let us love one an - oth - er, for love   is of God.

A7   D   Bm   Em   A   D   Bm   Em   A A7   D

Be - lov-ed, let us love one an - oth - er, for God   is love.

Text and music: Samuel Batt Owens (1928-1998)

138   There in God's Garden

1 There in God's gar - den stands the Tree of Wis - dom,
2 Its name is Je - sus, name that says, "Our Sa - vior!"
3 Thorns not its own are tan - gled in its fo - liage;
4 See how its branch - es reach to us in wel - come;
5 This is my end - ing, this my re - sur - rec - tion:

whose leaves hold forth the heal - ing of the na -
There on its branch - es see the scars of suf -
our greed has starved it, our de - spite has choked
hear what the Voice says, "Come to me, ye wear -
in - to your hands, Lord, I com - mit my spir -

tions: Tree of all know - ledge, Tree of all com -
fering; see where the ten - drils of our hu - man
it. Yet, look! It lives! Its grief has not de -
y! Give me your sick - ness, give me all your
it. This have I searched for; now I can pos -

Text: Király Imre von Pécselyi (c.1590-c.1641), Hungarian; tr. Erik Routley (1917-1982)
Music: K. Lee Scott (b. 1950)

Tr. © 1976, Hinshaw Music, Inc.; music © 1987, MorningStar Music Publishers

11 11 11 5
SHADES MOUNTAIN

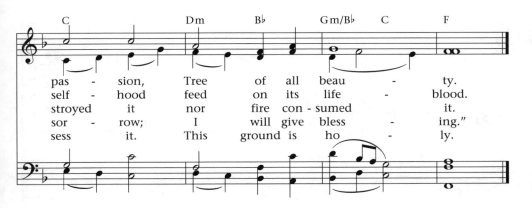

pas - sion, Tree of all beau - ty.
self - hood feed on its life - blood.
stroyed it nor fire con - sumed it.
sor - row; I will give bless - ing."
sess it. This ground is ho - ly.

6   All heaven is singing, "Thanks to Christ whose Passion
    offers in mercy healing, strength, and pardon.
    Peoples and nations, take it, take it freely!"
        Amen! Our Savior!

Holy God   139

Ho - ly, ho - ly, ho - ly God, ho - ly al - might - y God,

ho - ly, ho - ly, ho - ly al - might - y God, have mer - cy up - on us.

Text and music: Traditional Orthodox liturgy; harm. Alfred V. Fedak (b. 1953)
Harm. © 2000, Alfred V. Fedak

AGIOS, O THEOS

140 Calvary

Capo 2
Refrain Bm(Am)   F♯(E)

Cal - va - ry,   Cal - va - ry,   Cal - va -

Bm(Am)

ry,   Cal - va - ry,   Cal - va - ry,

F♯7(E7) Bm(Am)

Cal - va - ry,   sure - ly he died on   Cal - va - ry.

Unison or Solo

1 Ev - ery time I   think a - bout Je - sus,
2 Sin - ner, do you   love___ my Je - sus?
3 Don't you hear him   call - ing his Fa - ther?
4 Don't you hear him   say, "It is fin - ished!"
5 Je - sus died for   my___ sal - va - tion,

ev - ery time I   think a - bout Je - sus,
Sin - ner, do you   love___ my Je - sus?
Don't you hear him   call - ing his Fa - ther?
Don't you hear him   say, "It is fin - ished!"
Je - sus died for   my___ sal - va - tion,

Text and music: African-American spiritual

CALVARY

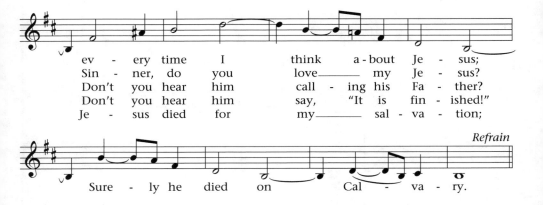

ev - ery time I think a - bout Je - sus;
Sin - ner, do you love_____ my Je - sus?
Don't you hear him call - ing his Fa - ther?
Don't you hear him say, "It is fin - ished!"
Je - sus died for my_____ sal - va - tion;

Refrain

Sure - ly he died on Cal - va - ry.

Why Has God Forsaken Me? 141

1 "Why has God for - sak - en me?" Je - sus cried out from the cross,
2 At the tomb of Laz - a - rus Je - sus wept with o - pen grief.
3 Je - sus, as his life ex - pired, placed him - self with - in God's care.
4 Mys-tery shrouds our life and death, but we need not be a - fraid,

as he shared the lone - li - ness of our deep - est grief and loss.
Grant us, God, the tears which heal all our pain and un - be - lief.
At our dy - ing, Christ, may we trust the love which con-quers fear.
for the mys-tery's heart is love, God's great love which Christ dis-played.

Text: William L. Wallace (b. 1933)
Music: Taihei Sato (b. 1936)

Text © 1981, Selah Publishing Co., Inc.; music © 1983, Taihei Sato

77 77
SHIMPI

142 Psalm 22

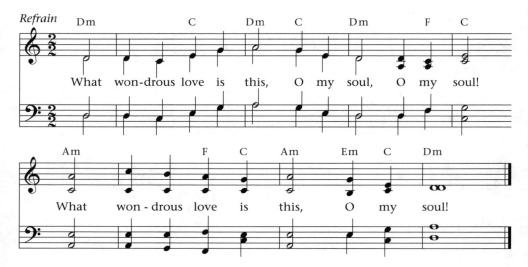

Refrain

What won-drous love is this, O my soul, O my soul!
What won-drous love is this, O my soul!

Refrain

Voice One

1 My God, my God, why have you forsaken me?

  Why are you so far from helping me,
    from the words of my groaning?
2 O my God, I cry by day, but you do not answer;

  and by night, but find no rest.

Voice Two

3 Yet you are holy,
    enthroned on the praises of Israel.
4 In you our ancestors trusted;
    they trusted, and you delivered them.
5 To you they cried, and were saved;
    in you they trusted, and were not put to shame.

Voice One

6 But I am a worm, and not human;
    scorned by others, and despised by the people.
7 All who see me mock at me;
    they make mouths at me, they shake their heads;

8 "Commit your cause to the LORD; let him deliver—
    let him rescue the one in whom he delights!"

Voice Two

9 Yet it was you who took me from the womb;
    you kept me safe on my mother's breast.
10 On you I was cast from my birth,
    and since my mother bore me you have been my God.
11 Do not be far from me,
    for trouble is near
    and there is no one to help.

Refrain

Voice One

22 I will tell of your name to my brothers and sisters;
    in the midst of the congregation I will praise you:
23 You who fear the LORD, praise him!
All you offspring of Jacob, glorify him;
    stand in awe of him, all you offspring of Israel!

Refrain text: S. Mead's *A General Selection* (1811)
Music: W. Walker's *Southern Harmony* (1835); arr. Emily R. Brink (b. 1940)
Arr. © 1987, CRC Publications

WONDROUS LOVE

Voice Two
24 For he did not despise or abhor
  the affliction of the afflicted;
he did not hide his face from me,
  but heard when I cried to him.
25 **From you comes my praise in the great
  congregation;
  my vows I will pay before those who
  fear him.**
26 **The poor shall eat and be satisfied;
  those who seek him shall praise the
  Lord.
  May your hearts live forever!**

Voice One
27 All the ends of the earth shall remember
  and turn to the Lord;
and all the families of the nations
  shall worship before him.

28 **For dominion belongs to the Lord,
  and he rules over the nations.**

Voice Two
29 To him, indeed, shall all who sleep in the
  earth bow down;
  before him shall bow all who go down
  to the dust,
  and I shall live for him.
30 **Posterity will serve him;
  future generations will be told about
  the Lord,**
31 **and proclaim his deliverance to a people
  yet unborn,
  saying that he has done it.**

Refrain

Jesus, Remember Me

143

Text: Luke 23:42
Music: Jacques Berthier (1923-1994)

JESUS, REMEMBER ME

© 1978, 1980, 1981, Les Presses de Taizé (France), admin. GIA Publications, Inc.

144 Now Behold the Lamb

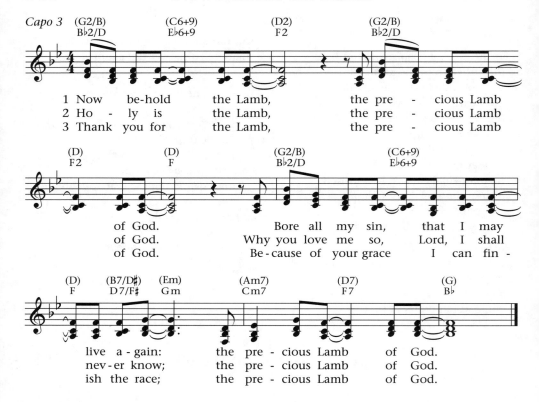

1 Now be-hold the Lamb, the pre - cious Lamb
2 Ho - ly is the Lamb, the pre - cious Lamb
3 Thank you for the Lamb, the pre - cious Lamb

of God. Bore all my sin, that I may
of God. Why you love me so, Lord, I shall
of God. Be-cause of your grace I can fin -

live a - gain: the pre - cious Lamb of God.
nev - er know; the pre - cious Lamb of God.
ish the race; the pre - cious Lamb of God.

Refrain (sing st. 1 above)

Surely he has borne our infirmities
  and carried our diseases;
but he was wounded for our transgressions,
  crushed for our iniquities,
upon him was the punishment that made
  us whole,
  and by his bruises we are healed.
All we like sheep have gone astray;
  we have all turned to our own way,
and the Lord has laid on him
  the iniquity of us all.
He was oppressed, and he was afflicted,
  yet he did not open his mouth;
like a lamb that is led to the slaughter,
and like a sheep that before its shearers is
  silent,
so he did not open his mouth.

Refrain (st. 2)

Out of his anguish he shall see light.
The righteous one, my servant, shall make
  many righteous,
  And he will bear their iniquities.
Therefore I will allot him a portion with
  the great,
because he poured out himself to death,
  and was numbered with the transgressors.

—from Isaiah 53

Worthy is the Lamb that was slaughtered
to receive power and wealth and wisdom
  and might
and honor and glory and might
forever and ever. Amen.

—Revelation 5:12

Refrain (st. 3)

Text and music: Kirk Franklin (b. 1970)

There Is a Redeemer

1 There is a Re - deem - er, Je - sus, God's own Son;
2 Je - sus, my Re - deem - er, name a - bove all names,
3 When I stand in glo - ry I will see his face;

pre - cious Lamb of God, Mes - si - ah, Ho - ly One.
pre - cious Lamb of God, Mes - si - ah, hope for sin - ners slain.
there I'll serve my King for - ev - er, in that ho - ly place.

Refrain

Thank you, O my Fa - ther, for giv - ing us your Son, and

leav - ing your Spir - it till the work on earth is done.

Text and music: Melody Green (b.1946)

146   Psalm 118

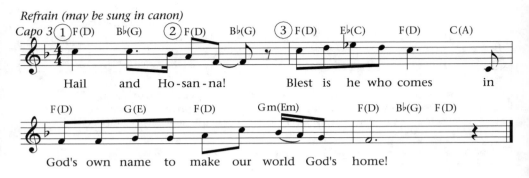

Hail and Ho-san-na! Blest is he who comes in

God's own name to make our world God's home!

Refrain

1 O give thanks to the LORD, for he is good;
   his steadfast love endures forever!
2 Let Israel say,
   "His steadfast love endures forever."
4 Let those who fear the LORD say,
   "His steadfast love endures forever."

Refrain

14 The LORD is my strength and my might;
   he has become my salvation.
15 **There are glad songs of victory in the
   tents of the righteous:**
   **"The right hand of the LORD does
   valiantly;**
16   **the right hand of the LORD is exalted;
   the right hand of the LORD does
   valiantly."**
17 I shall not die, but I shall live,
   and recount the deeds of the LORD.
18 The LORD has punished me severely,
   but he did not give me over to death.
19 **Open to me the gates of righteousness,
   that I may enter through them
   and give thanks to the LORD.**
20 This is the gate of the LORD;
   the righteous shall enter through it.

Refrain

21 I thank you that you have answered me
   and have become my salvation.
22 The stone that the builders rejected
   has become the chief cornerstone.
23 **This is the LORD's doing;
   it is marvelous in our eyes.**
24 This is the day that the LORD has made;
   let us rejoice and be glad in it.
25 **Save us, we beseech you, O LORD!
   O LORD, we beseech you, give us
   success!**
26 Blessed is the one who comes in the name
   of the LORD.
   We bless you from the house of the
   LORD.
27 **The LORD is God,
   and he has given us light.**
   Bind the festal procession with branches,
   up to the horns of the altar.
28 **You are my God, and I will give thanks to
   you;
   you are my God, I will extol you.**
29 O give thanks to the LORD, for he is good,
   for his steadfast love endures forever.

Refrain

Refrain text: James L. H. Brumm (b. 1962)
Music: Alfred V. Fedak (b. 1953)

Christ Is Risen

1 Christ is ris - en! Shout ho - san - na! Cel - e - brate this day of days!
2 Christ is ris - en! Raise your spir - its from the cav - erns of des - pair.
3 Christ is ris - en! Earth and heav - en nev - er - more shall be the same.

Christ is ris - en! Hush in won - der; all cre - a - tion is a - mazed.
Walk with glad - ness in the morn - ing. See what love can do and dare.
Break the bread of new cre - a - tion where the world is still in pain.

In the de - sert all - sur - round - ing, see, a spread - ing tree has grown.
Drink the wine of res - ur - rec - tion, not a ser - vant, but a friend.
Tell its grim, de - mon - ic cho - rus: "Christ is ris - en! Get you gone!"

Heal - ing leaves of grace a - bound - ing bring a taste of love un - known.
Je - sus is our strong com - pan - ion. Joy and peace shall nev - er end.
God the First and Last is with us. Sing ho - san - na ev - ery - one!

Text: Brian Wren (b. 1936)
Music: Polish carol; arr. *Psalter Hymnal* (1987)
Text © 1986, Hope Publishing Co.; arr. © 1987, CRC Publications

87 87 88 77
W ZLOBIE LEZY

148 Celtic Alleluia

Text and music: Fintan O'Carroll (1922-1981) and Christopher Walker (b. 1947)

Alternative stanzas

1 Father, we praise you as Lord. All of the earth gives you glory,
for your majesty fills the heavens, fills the earth! *Refrain*

2 Go, with the power of Christ, proclaiming to all "He is risen!
And he lives today at the right hand of God!" *Refrain*

3 Now we are called to go forth, filled with the power of the Spirit,
to serve everyone in the name of the Lord! *Refrain*

Aleluya / Alleluia 149

2 Alleluia. Alleluia. *(3x)*
Christ, the first-fruits from the grave.

3 Alleluia. Alleluia. *(3x)*
Christ has given us new life.

4 Alleluia. Alleluia. *(3x)*
Glory, love, and praise to God.

Text and music: Honduras; arr. John L. Bell (b. 1949)

Arr. © 1995, WGRG the Iona Community (Scotland), admin. GIA Publications, Inc.

150   Alleluia! Jesus Is Risen!

1 Alleluia! Jesus is risen! Trumpets resounding in glorious light! Splendor, the Lamb, heaven forever! Oh, what a miracle God has in sight!

2 Walking the way, Christ in the center telling the story to open our eyes; breaking our bread, giving us glory: Jesus our blessing, our constant surprise.

3 Jesus the vine, we are the branches; life in the Spirit the fruit of the tree; heaven to earth, Christ to the people, gift of the future now flowing to me.

4 Weeping, be gone; sorrow be silent: death put asunder, and Easter is bright. Cherubim sing: "O grave, be open!" Clothe us in wonder, adorn us in light.

5 City of God, Easter forever, golden Jerusalem, Jesus the Lamb, river of life, saints and archangels, sing with creation to God the I AM!

Text: Herbert F. Brokering (b. 1926)
Music: David N. Johnson (1922-1987)

45 10 D with refrain
EARTH AND ALL STARS

Text from *With One Voice*, © 1995, Augsburg Fortress; music © 1969 *Contemporary Worship I: Hymns*, Augsburg Fortress

Je - sus is ris - en and we shall a - rise:

give God the glo - ry! Al - le - lu - ia!

He's Alive! 151

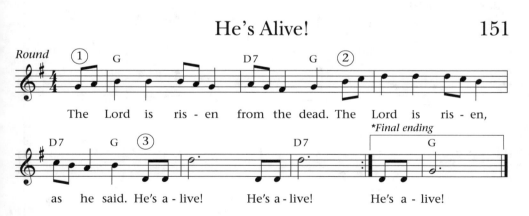

The Lord is ris - en from the dead. The Lord is ris - en,

as he said. He's a - live! He's a - live! He's a - live!

After group ③ is finished, everyone sings the final ending together.

Text and music: Tom Fettke (b. 1941)

152   I Am the Bread of Life

Solo 1 I am the bread of life;— they who come to me shall not—
Solo 2 The bread that I will give— is my flesh for the life of the
Solo 3 I am the res - ur - rec-tion;— I— am the—
All 4 Yes, Lord,— we be - lieve— that— you— are the—

hun - ger; they who be - lieve in me shall not thirst.
world,— and they who eat— of this bread,
life.— They who be - lieve— in me,
Christ,— the— Son— of God

No one can come to me— un - less the Fa - ther draws them.
they shall— live for - ev - er,— they shall live for - ev - er.
e - ven— if they die,— they shall live for - ev - er.
who— has come— in - to— the— world.—

Refrain

And I will raise them up, and I will raise them

up, and I will raise them up on the last day.

Text: Suzanne Toolan (b. 1927), based on John 6:35, 44; 11:25
Music: Suzanne Toolan; harm. Betty Pulkingham (b. 1928)

© 1970, GIA Publications, Inc.

Come to Us, Beloved Stranger

1 Come to us, be-lov-ed Stran-ger, as you came that Eas-ter day.
2 Stay with us and give us bless-ing, that our hopes a-gain may rise.
3 We would nev-er fail to see you as you walk with us each day.

Walk with us to our Em-ma-us, for we need you still to-day.
Of-fer us your bro-ken bo-dy; o-pen our un-see-ing eyes.
As a friend and not a stran-ger you would join us on our way.

Come to us when we are bro-ken, when our dear-est hopes are lost.
Come to us, God's love em-bod-ied; touch our hearts with burn-ing flame.
Help us trust that through your mer-cy we can doubt and fear tran-scend,

Speak to us the proph-ets' mes-sage you ful-filled up-on the cross.
Ris-en Christ, once dead, now liv-ing, come to us through joy, through pain.
and to oth-ers be a bless-ing. Keep us faith-ful till life's end.

Text: Edith Sinclair Downing (b. 1922)
Music: *Sacred Harp* (1844); harm. A. Royce Eckhardt (b. 1937)
Text © 1993, Edith Sinclair Downing; harm. © 1972, 1996, Covenant Publications

87 87 D
BEACH SPRING

154   God Has Gone Up with Shouts of Joy!

Text: James L. H. Brumm (b. 1962)
Music: Bohemian Brethren's *Kirchengesänge* (1556); harm. Heinrich Riemann (19th cent.);
 desc. Charles H. Webb (b. 1933)

87 87 887
MIT FREUDEN ZART

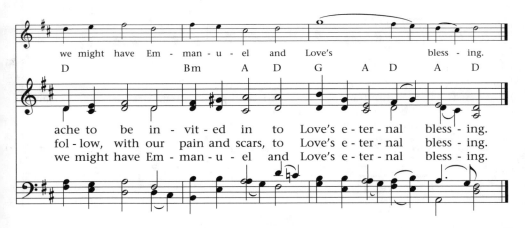

| we might have | Em - man - u - el | and | Love's | | | | bless - ing. |
| D | Bm | A | D | G | A | D | A | D |

| ache to be in - vit - ed in to Love's e - ter - nal bless - ing. |
| fol - low, with our pain and scars, to Love's e - ter - nal bless - ing. |
| we might have Em - man - u - el and Love's e - ter - nal bless - ing. |

Psalm 16   155

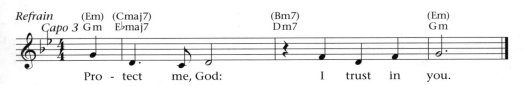

Refrain   (Em) (Cmaj7)   (Bm7)   (Em)
Capo 3 Gm Ebmaj7   Dm7   Gm

Pro - tect me, God: I trust in you.

Refrain

1 Protect me, O God, for in you I take
refuge.

2 I say to the LORD, "You are my Lord;
I have no good apart from you."

3 **As for the holy ones in the land, they are
the noble,**
in whom is all my delight.

4 Those who choose another god multiply
their sorrows;
their drink offerings of blood I will not
pour out
or take their names upon my lips.

Refrain

5 The LORD is my chosen portion and my
cup;
you hold my lot.

6 The boundary lines have fallen for me in
pleasant places;
I have a goodly heritage.

7 **I bless the LORD who gives me counsel;
in the night also my heart instructs me.**

8 I keep the LORD always before me;
because he is at my right hand, I shall
not be moved.

Refrain

9 Therefore my heart is glad, and my soul
rejoices;
my body also rests secure.

10 **For you do not give me up to Sheol,
or let your faithful one see the Pit.**

11 You show me the path of life.
In your presence there is fullness of joy;
in your right hand are pleasures
forevermore.

Refrain

Refrain text: Michael Saward (b. 1932)
Music: M. Christian T. Strover (b. 1932)

MEPHIBOSHETH

156 Psalm 47: Clap Your Hands All You Nations

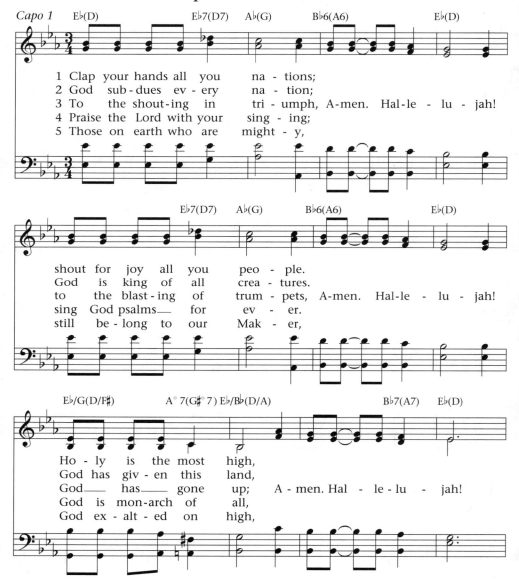

1 Clap your hands all you na - tions;
2 God sub - dues ev - ery na - tion;
3 To the shout-ing in tri - umph, A-men. Hal-le - lu - jah!
4 Praise the Lord with your sing - ing;
5 Those on earth who are might - y,

shout for joy all you peo - ple.
God is king of all crea - tures.
to the blast - ing of trum - pets, A-men. Hal-le - lu - jah!
sing God psalms for ev - er.
still be - long to our Mak - er,

Ho - ly is the most high,
God has giv - en this land,
God has gone up; A - men. Hal - le-lu - jah!
God is mon-arch of all,
God ex - alt - ed on high,

Text: Psalm 47; para. The Iona Community
Music: John Bell (b. 1949)

MARIUS

might-y o - ver the earth.
to the peo-ple he loves.
God as-cends o - ver all. A - men. Hal - le - lu - jah!
sov - 'reign o - ver the earth.
God, for - ev - er our Lord.

Lord, I Lift Your Name on High 157

Lord, I lift your name on high; Lord, I love to sing your prais-es.
I'm so glad you're in my life; I'm so glad you came to save us.

You came from heav - en to earth to show the way, from the earth

to the cross, my debt to pay, from the cross to the

grave, from the grave to the sky. Lord, I lift your name on high!

Text and music: Rick Founds (b. 1954)
© 1989, Maranatha Praise, Inc., admin. The Copyright Company

LORD, I LIFT YOUR NAME

158 You Are Crowned with Many Crowns

Text and music: John Sellers (b. 1954)
© 1984, Integrity's Hosanna! Music

power - er and reign in glo - ry! You are the Lord of heav - en and earth! You are Lord of all. You are Lord of all.

Easter Prayer of Adoration 159

Glory to you, O God:

**On this day you won victory over death.
raising Jesus from the grave and giving us
eternal life.**

Glory to you, O Christ:

**For us and for our salvation
you overcame death
and opened the gate to everlasting life.**

Glory to you, O Holy Spirit:

**You lead us into truth
and bring us to new life.**

**Glory to you, O Blessed Trinity,
now and forever. Amen.**

160

He Is Lord

Text and music: Anonymous; harm. Dale Grotenhuis (b. 1931)
Harm. © 1987 CRC Publications

HE IS LORD

I'm Gonna Sing When the Spirit Says Sing 161

* pray, cry, shout

Text and music: African-American spiritual; arr. William Farley Smith (b. 1941)

Arr. © 1989, The United Methodist Publishing House, admin. The Copyright Company

162   On the Day of Pentecost

The crowd gathered and was bewildered,
because each one heard the disciples
    speaking
in the native language of each.
Amazed and astonished, they asked:

Are not all these who are speaking
    Galileans?
How is it that we hear, each of us,
in our own native language?
In our own languages we hear them
    speaking
about God's deeds of power.

Then Peter, standing with the eleven,
    addressed them:
"This is what was spoken through the
    prophet Joel:

Speaker 1 (in English)
In the last days it will be, God declares,
that I will pour out my Spirit upon all flesh.
Then everyone who calls on the name of
    the Lord will be saved.

Speaker 2 (in Spanish)
Sucederá que en los últimos días—dice
    Dios—derramaré mi Espíritu sobre todo
    el género humano.
Y todo el que invoque el nombre del Señor
    será salvo.

*(Other speakers may continue in various
languages.)*

—from Acts 2

163   Send Us Your Spirit

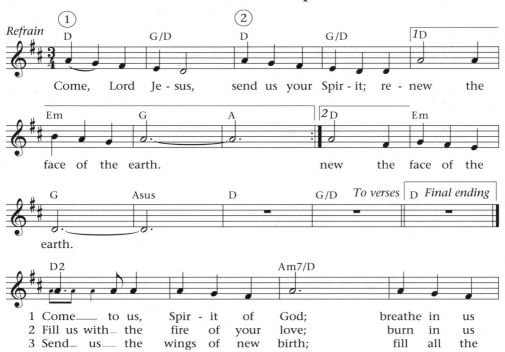

Refrain
Come, Lord Je-sus, send us your Spir-it; re-new the face of the earth. new the face of the earth.

1 Come to us, Spir-it of God; breathe in us
2 Fill us with the fire of your love; burn in us
3 Send us the wings of new birth; fill all the

Text and music: David Haas (b. 1957)

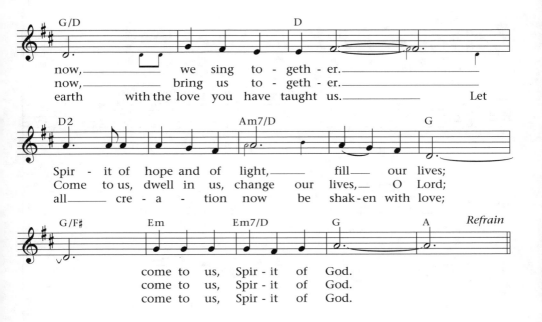

now,_____ we sing to - geth - er._____
now,_____ bring us to - geth - er._____
earth with the love you have taught us._____ Let

Spir - it of hope and of light,____ fill____ our lives;
Come to us, dwell in us, change our lives,__ O Lord;
all____ cre - a - tion now be shak - en with love;

come to us, Spir - it of God.
come to us, Spir - it of God.
come to us, Spir - it of God.

Refrain

Psalm 104   164

Refrain (163 Refrain only)

²⁴O LORD, how manifold are your works!
  In wisdom you have made them all;
  the earth is full of your creatures.
²⁵Yonder is the sea, great and wide,
  creeping things innumerable are there,
  living things both small and great.
²⁶**There go the ships,**
  and Leviathan that you formed to sport
  in it.

²⁷These all look to you
  to give them their food in due season;
²⁸**when you give to them, they gather it up;**
  when you open your hand, they are
filled with good things.
²⁹When you hide your face, they are
  dismayed;
  when you take away their breath, they
  die
  and return to their dust.

³⁰**When you send forth your spirit, they are**
  created;
  and you renew the face of the ground.

Refrain

³¹May the glory of the LORD endure
  forever;
  may the LORD rejoice in his works—
³²**who looks on the earth and it trembles,**
  who touches the mountains and they
  smoke.
³³I will sing to the LORD as long as I live;
  I will sing praise to my God while I have
  being.
³⁴**May my meditation be pleasing to him,**
  for I rejoice in the LORD.
³⁵Let sinners be consumed from the earth,
  and let the wicked be no more.
  Bless the LORD, O my soul.
  Praise the LORD!

Refrain

165

Come, Holy Spirit

Refrain

Leader

Come, Ho - ly Spir - it.

(Fine) All

Come, Ho - ly Spir - it.

Come, Ho - ly Spir - it.

Come Ho - ly Spir - it.

Ma - ra - na - tha!

Ma - ra - na - tha!

Fine

Come, Lord, come.

Come, Lord, come.

Refrain: John Bell (b. 1949)

© 1995, WGRG the Iona Community (Scotland), admin. GIA Publications, Inc.

Gracious Spirit

1 Gra-cious Spir - it, heed our plead - ing; fash - ion us all a - new.
2 Come to teach us; come to nour - ish those who be - lieve in Christ.
3 Guide our think - ing and our speak - ing done in your ho - ly name.
4 Not mere knowl-edge, but dis - cern - ment, nor root-less lib - er - ty;
5 Keep us fer - vent in our wit - ness; un-swayed by earth's al - lure.

It's your lead - ing that we're need-ing; help us to fol - low you.
Bless the faith-ful; may they flour-ish, strength-ened by grace un - priced.
Mo - ti - vate all in their seek-ing, free - ing from guilt and shame.
turn dis - qui - et to con - tent-ment, doubt in - to cer - tain - ty.
Ev - er grant us zeal - ous fit - ness, which you a - lone as - sure.

Refrain

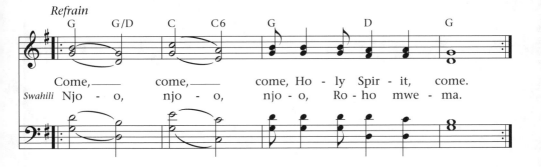

Come,— come,— come, Ho - ly Spir - it, come.
Swahili Njo - o, njo - o, njo - o, Ro - ho mwe - ma.

Text and music: Wilson Niwagila (20th cent.), Tanzania; tr. Howard S. Olson (b. 1922);
  arr. C. Michael Hawn (b. 1948)

CM with refrain
NJOO KWETU, ROHO MWEMA

© Lutheran Theological College, Makumira, Tanzania, admin. Augsburg Fortress

167 Gift of Christ from God Our Father

Descant
4 Gift of Christ for our sal-va-tion, come, Spir-it, come!

Capo 3 F(D) B♭(G) Gm(Em) C(A) F(D) B♭(G) C(A) F(D)

1 Gift of Christ from God our Fa-ther, come, Spir-it, come!
2 Gift of Christ to guide and teach us, come, Spir-it, come!
3 Gift of Christ to help us pray-ing, come, Spir-it, come!
4 Gift of Christ for our sal-va-tion, come, Spir-it, come!

Bring to birth your new cre-a-tion, come, Spir-it, come! All the

F(D) B♭(G) Gm(Em) C(A) F(D) B♭(G) C(A) F(D) B♭(G) F(D)

Well of life and gen-erous giv-er, come, Spir-it, come! With your
Coun-sel-or so swift to reach us, come, Spir-it, come! Christ is
Ad-vo-cate be-side us stay-ing, come, Spir-it, come! In the
Bring to birth your new cre-a-tion, come, Spir-it, come! All the

Text: David Mowbray (b.1938)
Music: Welsh melody (c. 1784); desc. Hal Hopson (b.1933)

Text © 1999, Jubilate Hymns Ltd., admin. Hope Publishing; desc. © GIA Publications, Inc.

84 84 88 84
AR HYD Y NOS

de - vil's work un - do - ing, Christ a - lone pur - su - ing,

(G) (D) (G) (Am) (G) (D) (Em) (D) (Em) (Bm) (Em) (Asus) (A)
B♭ F B♭ Cm B♭ F Gm F Gm Dm Gm Csus C

light our minds en - light - en, with your grace our tal - ents height-en,
Lord, so may we name him, nev - er fear - ful - ly dis - claim him,
work of in - ter - ces - sion, in the heal-ing of con - fes - sion,
dev - il's work un - do - ing, Christ's own min - is - try pur - su - ing,

glo - ry in the Church re - new - ing! Come, Spir - it, come!

F(D) B♭(G) Gm(Em) C(A) F(D) B♭(G) C(A) F(D)

with your joy our wor - ship bright-en, come, Spir - it, come!
but to all the world pro-claim him. Come, Spir - it, come!
in suc-cess and in de - pres - sion, come, Spir - it, come!
glo - ry in the Church re - new - ing! Come, Spir - it, come!

168 Santo Espíritu, excelsa paloma / Holy Spirit, from Heaven Descended

Text and music: Philip W. Blycker (b. 1939)

XCELSA PALOMA

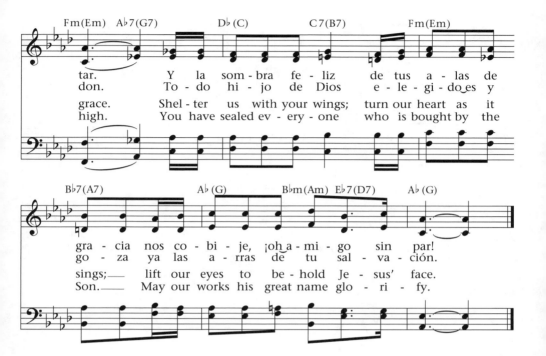

Fm(Em)　A♭7(G7)　D♭(C)　C7(B7)　Fm(Em)

tar.　Y la som - bra fe - liz de tus a - las de
don.　To - do hi - jo de Dios e - le - gi - do es y
grace.　Shel - ter us with your wings; turn our heart as it
high.　You have sealed ev - ery - one who is bought by the

B♭7(A7)　A♭(G)　B♭m(Am)　E♭7(D7)　A♭(G)

gra - cia nos co - bi - je, ¡oh a - mi - go sin par!
go - za ya las a - rras de tu sal - va - ción.
sings;___ lift our eyes to be - hold Je - sus' face.
Son.___ May our works his great name glo - ri - fy.

3 Santo Espíritu, aceite bendito,
cual producto del verde olivar;
luminaria y calor
en la tienda sagrada
donde Aarón se acercaba a adorar.
Agua viva y regeneradora,
sanctifícanos contra el mal;
somos uno en Jesús,
los creyentes del mundo,
por tu santa labor bautismal.

4 Santo Espíritu, viento potente,
fuente y fuerza de paz y de amor;
paracleto veraz
que consuelo nos brindas
y abogas a nuestro favor.
Sénos luz que ilumine la Biblia,
nuestros pies dirigiendo al andar.
Hoy rendimos a ti
nuestras almas ansiosas;
sólo ungidos podremos triunfar.

3 Holy Spirit, flow freely among us,
sacred oil giving sight where sin blinds;
just as Aaron of old
lit the lamps in the cold,
warm our hearts and illumine our minds.
You have baptized us into one body;
Living Water, now cleanse and renew.
Sanctify us, we pray,
that God's Word we obey,
and to Christ may we ever be true.

4 Holy Spirit of God, breathe upon us;
fill our hearts with your love, joy, and peace.
Paraclete, you are nigh,
interceding on high;
grant that our meager faith would increase.
Be our lamp to interpret the Scriptures,
be our guide to instruct in the way.
We surrender our will
as our cup you refill
to victoriously live every day.

169 Wind Who Makes All Winds That Blow

1 Wind who makes all winds that blow— gusts that bend the
2 Fire who fuels all fires that burn— suns a-round which
3 Ho-ly Spir-it, wind and flame, move with-in our

sap-lings low, gales that heave the sea in waves,
plan-ets turn, bea-cons mark-ing reefs and shoals,
mor-tal frame. Make our hearts an al-tar pyre;

stir-rings in the mind's deep caves— aim your breath with
shin-ing truth to guide our souls— come to us as
kin-dle them with your own fire. Breathe and blow up-

stead-y power on your church, this day, this hour. Raise, re-
once you came; burst in tongues of sa-cred flame! Light and
on that blaze till our lives, our deeds, and ways speak that

Text: Thomas H. Troeger (b. 1945)
Music: Joseph Parry (1841-1903)

Text © 1994, Oxford University Press, Inc.

77 77 D
ABERYSTWYTH

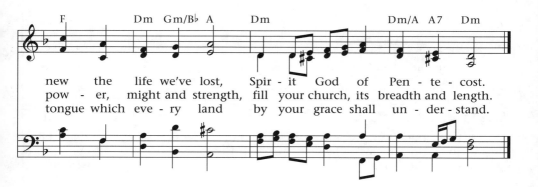

new   the   life we've lost,   Spir - it   God   of   Pen - te - cost.
pow - er,   might and strength,   fill   your church, its   breadth and length.
tongue which eve - ry   land   by   your grace shall   un - der - stand.

Litany for Pentecost   170

Holy Spirit, Lord and Giver of Life:
At the beginning of time you moved over
   the face of the waters;
you breathe into every living being the
   breath of life.
**Come, Creator Spirit, and renew the whole
   creation.**

Holy Spirit, voice of the prophets:
You enflame men and women with a
   passion for your truth,
and through them call your people
to the ways of justice and compassion.
**Come, Spirit of Righteousness, and burn in
   our hearts.**

Holy Spirit, Spirit of Jesus:
By your power Jesus came to bring good
news to the poor
and release to those held captive.
**Come, Liberating Spirit, and free us from
   the powers of sin and death.**

Holy Spirit, Advocate, Teacher:
You speak to us of our Lord
and show us the depth of his love.
**Come, Spirit of Truth, abide in us and lead
   us in the way of Jesus Christ.**

Holy Spirit, Wind and Flame:
You filled disciples with joy and courage,
empowering them to preach your word
and to share your good news.
**Come, Spirit of Power, make us bold
   witnesses of your redeeming love.**

Holy Spirit, Spirit of Peace:
You break down barriers of language, race
   and culture,
and heal the divisions that separate us.
**Come, Reconciling Spirit, and unite us all
   in the love of Christ.**

Holy Spirit, Lord and Giver of Life:
At the close of the age
all creation will be renewed to sing your
   praises.
**Come, Creator Spirit, and make us new
   creations in Jesus Christ.**

171   Like the Murmur of the Dove's Song

Descant

3 With the heal - ing of di - vi - sion, with the

Capo 3

1 Like the mur - mur of the dove's song, like the
2 To the mem - bers of Christ's bod - y, to the
3 With the heal - ing of di - vi - sion, with the

cease - less voice of prayer, with the power to love and

chal - lenge of her flight, like the vig - or of the
branch - es of the Vine, to the church in faith as -
cease - less voice of prayer, with the power to love and

wit - ness, with the peace be - yond com - pare:

wind's rush, like the new flame's ea - ger might:
sem - bled, to her midst as gift and sign:
wit - ness, with the peace be - yond com - pare:

Come, Ho - ly Spir - it, come.

Come, Ho - ly Spir - it, come.
Come, Ho - ly Spir - it, come.
Come, Ho - ly Spir - it, come.

Text: Carl P. Daw, Jr. (b. 1944)
Music: Peter Cutts (b. 1937); desc. Emily R. Brink (b. 1940)

87 87 6
BRIDEGROOM

Faith Begins by Letting Go

1 Faith be-gins by let-ting go, giv-ing up what had seemed sure,
2 Faith en-dures by hold-ing on, keep-ing mem-'ry's roots a-live
3 Faith ma-tures by reach-ing out, stretch-ing minds, en-larg-ing hearts,

tak-ing risks and press-ing on, though the way feels less se-cure:
so that hope may bear its fruit; prom-ise-fed, our souls will thrive,
shar-ing strug-gles, liv-ing prayer, bind-ing up the bro-ken parts;

pil-grim-age both right and odd, trust-ing all our life to God.
not through mer-it we pos-sess but by God's great faith-ful-ness.
till we find the com-mon-place ripe with wit-ness to God's grace.

Text: Carl P. Daw, Jr. (b. 1944)
Music: Charles F. Gounod (1818-1893)

77 77 77
LUX PRIMA

173   This Holy Covenant Was Made

1 This ho-ly cov-e-nant was made; God, our De-liv-
2 This ho-ly cov-e-nant was new at ta-ble with
3 This ho-ly cov-e-nant of flame sears in our hearts

erance, was o-beyed. Seas were part-ed; free-dom start-ed.
Christ's gath-ered few. Bless-ing spo-ken; bo-dy bro-ken.
the sav-ing name. Spir-it's fire, our de-sire.

By cloud and fire we were led. By quail and man-
By lift-ed cup our God for-gives. By Je-sus' grace
By wind and tongue the Church is sealed. By might and pow-

Descant

Al-le-lu — ia, al-le-lu — ia,

na we were fed. Al-le-lu — ia, al-le-lu — ia,
a-lone we live.
er here re-vealed.

Text: Sylvia Dunstan (1955-1993)
Music: *Geistliche Kirchengesänge*, Cologne (1623); desc. Dale Grotenhuis (b. 1931)

Text © 1991, GIA Publications, Inc.; desc. © 1992, Dale Grotenhuis

88 44 88 with alleluias
LASST UNS ERFREUEN

al - le - lu - ia, al - le - lu - ia, al - le - lu - ia.

al - le - lu - ia, al - le - lu - ia, al - le - lu - ia.

Psalm 114

174

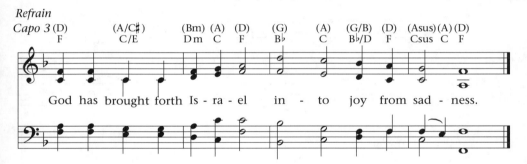

God has brought forth Is - ra - el in - to joy from sad - ness.

Refrain

Refrain

1 When Israel went out from Egypt,
    the house of Jacob from a people of
        strange language,
2 Judah became God's sanctuary,
    Israel his dominion.

3 **The sea looked and fled;**
    Jordan turned back.
4 **The mountains skipped like rams,**
    the hills like lambs.

Refrain

5 Why is it, O sea, that you flee?
    O Jordan, that you turn back?
6 O mountains, that you skip like rams?
    O hills, like lambs?

7 **Tremble, O earth, at the presence of the**
        LORD,
    at the presence of the God of Jacob,
8 **who turns the rock into a pool of water,**
    the flint into a spring of water.

Refrain

Refrain text: John of Damascus; tr. John Mason Neale (1818-1866)
Music: J. Horn's *Gesangbuch* (1544)

GAUDEAMUS PARITER

175   I Believe in God Almighty

1 I be-lieve in God Al-might-y, Fa-ther of all
2 I be-lieve that Je-sus suf-fered, scourged and scorned and
3 I be-lieve in God's own Spir-it, bond-ing all the

things that be, Mak-er of the earth and heav-ens,
cru-ci-fied, tak-en from the cross, was bur-ied–
saints with-in one Church, cath-o-lic and ho-ly,

Keep-er of the sky and sea. I be-lieve in
True Life there had tru-ly died. I be-lieve that
where for-give-ness frees from sin, in the bod-y's

God's Son, Je-sus, now for us both Lord and Christ, of the
on the third day Christ was raised up from the grave, then as-
res-ur-rec-tion, for the break-ing of death's chain gives the

Text: Sylvia Dunstan (1955-1993), based on the Apostles' Creed
Music: *Oude en Nieuwe Hollantse Boerenlities en Contradansen* (1710)

87 87 D

IN BABILONE

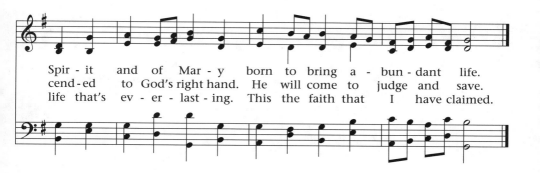

Spir - it and of Mar - y born to bring a - bun - dant life.
cend - ed to God's right hand. He will come to judge and save.
life that's ev - er - last - ing. This the faith that I have claimed.

My Only Comfort 176

What is your only comfort
in life and in death?

**That I am not my own,
but belong—
   body and soul,
   in life and in death—
to my faithful Savior, Jesus Christ.**

   **Christ has fully paid for all my sins with his precious blood,
   and has set me free from all the power of the devil.
   He also watches over me in such a way
   that not a hair can fall from my head
   without the will of my Father in heaven;
   in fact, all things must work together for my salvation.**

**Because I belong to him,
Christ, by his Holy Spirit,
assures me of eternal life
and makes me wholeheartedly willing and ready
from now on to live for him.**

—Heidelberg Catechism, Q&A 1

177 O Christ, the Great Foundation

1 O Christ, the great foun-da-tion on which your peo-ple stand
2 Bap-tized in one con-fes-sion, one Church in all the earth,
3 Where ty-rants' hold is tight-ened, where strong de-vour the weak,
4 This is the mo-ment glo-rious when he who once was dead

to preach your true sal-va-tion in ev-ery age and land,
we bear our Lord's im-pres-sion, the sign of sec-ond birth.
where in-no-cents are fright-ened, the righ-teous fear to speak,
shall lead his Church vic-to-rious, their cham-pion and their head.

pour out your Ho-ly Spir-it to make us strong and pure,
One ho-ly peo-ple gath-ered in love be-yond our own.
there let your church a-wak-ing at-tack the powers of sin,
The Lord of all cre-a-tion his heav'n-ly king-dom brings,

to keep the faith un-bro-ken as long as worlds en-dure.
By grace we were in-vit-ed; by grace we make you known.
and, all their ram-parts break-ing, with you the vic-to-ry win.
the fi-nal con-sum-ma-tion, the glo-ry of all things.

Text: Timothy T'ing Fang Lew (1892-1947), Chinese; tr. Mildred A Wiant (b. 1898)
Music: Samuel Sebastian Wesley (1810-1876)

76 76 D
AURELIA

We Are Members of Christ's Body

1 We are mem - bers of Christ's bod - y, joined by faith in
2 Ear and eye to one an - oth - er, we have need of
3 When one mem - ber suf - fers hard-ship, we will shoul - der

u - ni - ty: one in call - ing, joy, and suf-fering,
ev - ery part; hands and feet be - long to - geth - er,
all the pain; when an - oth - er part is hon - ored,

whole-some in di - ver - si - ty. We will work with
guid - ed by a loy - al heart; ten - dons, bones, and
joys through-out the bod - y reign; for our com - mon

gifts that dif - fer towards the King-dom's des - ti - ny.
flesh em-bod - y what the Spir - it's breath im - parts.
love is puls - ing towards the growth of Christ's do - main.

Text and music: Bert Polman (b. 1945)
© 1990, CRC Publications

87 87 87
FONTHILL

179 Somos uno en Cristo / We Are One in Christ

Spanish So-mos u-no en Cris-to, so-mos u-no, so-mos u-no,
English We are one in Christ Je-sus, all one bod-y, all one spir-it,

u-no só-lo. | só-lo. | Un so-lo Dios,
all to-geth-er. | geth-er. | We share one God,

un so-lo Se-ñor, u-na so-la fe,
one might-y Lord, one a-bid-ing faith,

un so-lo a-mor, un so-lo bau-tis-mo, un so-lo Es-
one bind-ing love, one sin-gle bap-tism, one Ho-ly

Text and music: Anonymous; tr. Alice Parker (b. 1925); arr. Philip W. Blycker (b. 1939)

Tr. © 1996, Abingdon Press; arr. © 1992, Celebremos/Libros Alianza

SOMOS UNO

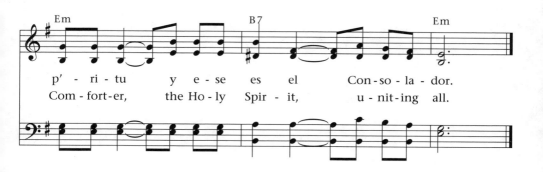

p' - ri - tu y e - se es el Con - so - la - dor.
Com - fort-er, the Ho - ly Spir - it, u - nit-ing all.

You Are My Hiding Place

180

Canon

You are my hid - ing place. You al - ways fill my heart with

songs of de - liv - er -ance. When-ev-er I am a - fraid I will trust in

you. I will trust in you. Let the weak say, "I am

strong in the strength of the Lord." Lord, I will trust in you."

Text and music: Michael Ledner (b. 1952)

181 Psalm 23

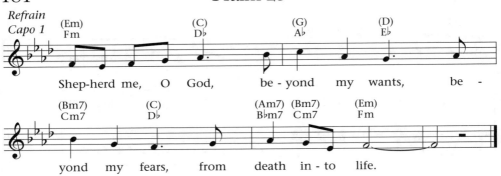

Refrain

1 The LORD is my shepherd, I shall not want.
2 He makes me lie down in green
      pastures;
he leads me beside still waters;
3 he restores my soul.
He leads me in right paths
   for his name's sake.

Refrain

4 Even though I walk through the darkest
      valley,
   I fear no evil;

for you are with me;
   your rod and your staff—
they comfort me.

Refrain

5 You prepare a table before me
   in the presence of my enemies;
you anoint my head with oil;
   my cup overflows.
6 Surely goodness and mercy shall follow me
   all the days of my life,
and I shall dwell in the house of the LORD
   my whole life long.

Refrain

Refrain: Marty Haugen (b. 1950)

© 1986, GIA Publications, Inc.

Alt. Refrain: Joseph Gelineau (b. 1920)

© 1963, Ladies of The Grail (England), admin. GIA Publications, Inc.

You, Lord, Are Both Lamb and Shepherd   182

Capo 5 (Am)

1 You, Lord, are both Lamb and Shep - herd.
2 Clothed in light up - on the moun - tain,
3 You, who walk each day be - side us,
4 Wor - thy is our earth - ly Je - sus!

You, Lord, are both prince and slave. You, peace - mak - er
stripped of might up - on the cross, shin - ing in e -
sit in pow - er at God's side. You, who preach a
Wor - thy is our cos - mic Christ! Wor - thy your de -

and sword - bring - er of the way you took and gave.
ter - nal glo - ry, beg - gar'd by a sol - dier's toss,
way that's nar - row, have a love that reach - es wide.
feat and vic - t'ry. Wor - thy still your peace and strife.

You, the ev - er - last - ing in - stant;
You, the ev - er - last - ing in - stant;
You, the ev - er - last - ing in - stant;
You, the ev - er - last - ing in - stant;

You, whom we both scorn and crave.
You, who are both gift and cost.
You, who are our pil - grim guide.
You, who are our death and life.

Text: Sylvia Dunstan (1955-1993)
Music: French, 17th cent.
Text © 1991, GIA Publications, Inc.

87 87 87
PICARDY

183

Psalm 46: God, Our Help
and Constant Refuge

1 God,   our help and   con-stant ref - uge,   ev - er pres-ent
2 Ho - ly riv - er   of God's cit - y,   heal - ing flows with -
3 God,   the Lord of   Hosts is with   us;   come,   be-hold these
4 Liv - ing Lord of   Hosts be with   us.   Come,   and fill   us

in   our   need, though the   earth   be ev - er   chang-ing, though it
in   your streams,   giv - ing strength with-in   our   cri - sis,   firm and
might-y   deeds: wars   are   end - ed, spears are   bro - ken;   at   this
with your power.   You   the   hope   of all   the   na - tions,   be   ex -

fall   in - to   the   sea: Rock   se - cure,   ev - er
stead - y   like   a   beam.   Na - tions   rage,   wars   to
voice   the world takes   heed.   Come,   O   Lord,   break   the
alt - ed   in   this   hour.   God Most   High,   lest   we

sure,   through all   tu - mult   you   en - dure.
wage;   God   will   still   pro - tect   this   age.
sword,   bring   us   peace   as   your   re - ward.
die,   give   us   hope   and   hear   our   cry.

Text: Psalm 46; vers. Fred Anderson (b. 1941)
Music: Herbert Howells (1892-1983)

87 87 337
MICHAEL

Psalm 84: How Lovely, Lord, How Lovely 184

1 How love-ly, Lord, how love-ly is your a-bid-ing place;
2 In your blest courts to wor-ship, O God, a sin-gle day
3 A sun and shield for-ev-er are you, O Lord most high;

my soul is long-ing, faint-ing, to feast up-on your grace.
is bet-ter than a thou-sand if I from you should stray.
you show-er us with bless-ings; no good will you de-ny.

The spar-row finds a shel-ter, a place to build her nest,
I'd rath-er keep the en-trance and claim you as my Lord
The saints, your grace re-ceiv-ing, from strength to strength shall go,

and so your tem-ple calls us with-in its walls to rest.
than rev-el in the rich-es the ways of sin af-ford.
and from their life shall riv-ers of bless-ing o-ver-flow.

Text: Psalm 84; vers. Arlo D. Duba (b. 1929)
Music: Hal H. Hopson (b. 1933)

76 76 D
MERLE'S TUNE

185

On Eagle's Wings

1 You who dwell in the shel-ter of the Lord, who a-
bide in his shad-ow for life, say to the Lord: "My
ref-uge, my rock in whom I trust!"

Refrain
And he will raise you up on ea-gle's wings, bear you on the
breath of dawn, make you to shine like the sun, and
hold you in the palm of his hand.

Text and music: Michael Joncas (b. 1951), based on Psalm 91

2 The snare of the fowl-er will nev-er cap-ture you, and fam - ine will bring you no fear: un-der his wings your ref - uge, his faith - ful - ness your shield. *Refrain*

3 You need not fear the ter-ror of the night, nor the ar - row that flies by day; though thou - sands fall a - bout you, near you it shall not come. *Refrain*

4 For to his an-gels is giv-en a com - mand to guard you in all of your ways; up - on their hands they will bear you up, lest you dash your foot a-gainst a stone.

186   Look and Learn

1 Look and learn from the birds of the air, fly - ing
2 Look and learn from the flowers of the field, bring - ing
3 What God wants should be our will; where God

high a-bove wor - ry and fear; nei - ther sow - ing nor
beau - ty and col - or to life; nei - ther sew - ing nor
calls should be our goal. When we seek the

har - vest-ing seed, yet they're gi - ven what - ev - er they need.
tai - lor-ing cloth, yet they're dressed in the fin - est at - tire.
king - dom first, all we've lost is ours a - gain.

Harmony

If the God of earth and heaven
If the God of earth and heaven
Let's be done with anx - ious thoughts,

cares for birds as much as this, won't he care much
cares for flowers as much as this, won't he care much
set a - side to-mor - row's cares, live each day that

Text and music: Nah Young-Soo, Korean; based on Matthew 6:23-24; tr. and arr. John Bell (b. 1949)
Eng. tr. and arr. © WGRG the Iona Community (Scotland), admin. GIA Publications, Inc.

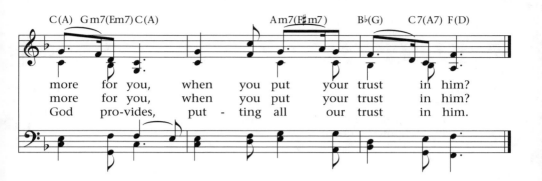

more for you, when you put your trust in him?
more for you, when you put your trust in him?
God pro-vides, put - ting all our trust in him.

In God Alone 187

In God a-lone my soul can find rest and peace, in

God my peace and joy. On - ly in God my

Fine

soul can find its rest, find its rest and peace. In

Text: based on Psalm 62:1
Music: Jacques Berthier (1923-1994)

188   Don'na Tokidemo / Anytime and Anywhere

Japanese 1 Don - 'na to-ki-de - mo, don - 'na to-ki-de -
        2 Don - 'na to-ki-de - mo, don - 'na to-ki-de -

English 1 An - y - time and an - y - where know that Je - sus' love is
      2 An - y time and an - y - where know that Je - sus' love is

mo ku - ru - shi - mi - ni ma - ke - zu, ku - ji -
mo shi - a - wa - se - o no - zo - mi, ku - ji -
there. When in grief and loss, when in pain, God will
there. Don't des - pair, for God is— kind. Look for

ke - te - wa na - ra - na - i. Ie - su sa - ma - no, Ie - su
ke - te - wa na - ra - na - i. Ie - su sa - ma - no, Ie - su
strength-en and— sus - tain. Put your hope in God; trust his
joy and you— will— find. Put a - way your fear; God is

sa - ma - no a - i o shi - n - ji - te.
sa - ma - no a - i ga a - ru - ka - ra.
ho - ly Word ev - ery time and ev - ery - where.
ver - y near ev - ery time and ev - ery - where.

Text: Junko Takahashi (1959-1967); tr. *Sing! A New Creation* (2001)
Music: Shin'ichi Takanami (b. 1941)

77 89 55 7
DON'NA TOKIDEMA

Through It All

Through it all, through it all, I've learned to trust in Je - sus; I've learned to trust in God.

Through it all, through it all, I've learned to de-pend up - on God's word.

Text and music: Andraé Crouch (b. 1945)

THROUGH IT ALL

190

Trust in the Lord

Capo 3

Trust in the Lord with all your heart, and lean not on your own un-der-stand - ing. In all your ways ac-knowl - edge God, and he will make straight your paths.

Text: Proverbs 3:5-6
Music: Barbara Boertje (b. 1959)

God Has Smiled on Me

Text and music: Isaiah Jones, Jr. (b. 1940)

© 1973, Davike Music Co./Fricout Music Co., admin. Fricon Entertainment

192 The Lord Is My Light

1 The Lord is my light, my light and my sal - va - tion. With God pro - tect - ing me from ev - ery dan - ger, whom shall I fear?

2 Should e - vil pow'rs ad - vance, should ar - mies try to kill, let them sur - round me and let them at - tack me; I'll still trust God.

3 One thing I ask the Lord, this on - ly I de - sire: Al - ways in wor - ship to gaze at God's good - ness and seek his aid.

4 Pre - served by God from harm, se - cure in him a - lone, I will re - joice in the face of af - flic - tion and sing God's song.

Text: The Iona Community, based on Psalm 27
Music: Czechoslovakian hymn tune (17th cent.)

Pues si vivimos / When We Are Living

Spanish 1 Pues si vi - vi - mos pa - ra él vi - vi - mos
2 En es - ta vi - da, fru - tos he - mos de dar

English 1 When we are liv - ing, it is in Christ Je - sus,
2 Through all our liv - ing, we our fruits must give.——

y si mo - ri - mos pa - ra él mo - ri - mos.
las o - bras bue - nas son pa - ra o - fren - dar.——
and when we're dy - ing, it is in the Lord.——
Good works of ser - vice are for of - fer - ing.——

Sea que vi - va - mos o que mu - ra - mos,
Ya sea que de - mos o que re - ci - ba - mos
Both in our liv - ing and in our dy - ing,
When we are giv - ing or when re - ceiv - ing,

so-mos del Se - ñor, so-mos del Se - ñor.
we be-long to God, we be-long to God.

3 En la tristeza y en el dolor,
en la belleza y en el amor,
sea que suframos o que gocemos
somos del Señor, somos del Señor.

4 En este mundo, hemos de encontrar
gente que llora y sin consolar.
Sea que ayudemos o que alimentemos
somos del Señor, somos del Señor.

3 'Mid times of sorrow and in times of pain,
when sensing beauty or in love's embrace,
whether we suffer or sing rejoicing,
we belong to God, we belong to God.

4 Across this wide world, we shall always find
those who are crying with no peace of mind.
But when we help them or when we feed them,
we belong to God, we belong to God.

Text: St. 1, Spanish, anonymous, tr. Elise S. Eslinger (b. 1942); st. 2-4, Roberto Escamilla (b. 1931),
tr. George Lockwood (b. 1946)
Music: Spanish melody

10 10 10 10
SOMOS DEL SENOR

194   A Cloud of Witnesses

After this I looked, and there was a great multitude
that no one could count, from every nation,
from all tribes and peoples and languages,
standing before the throne and before the Lamb,
robed in white, with palm branches in their hands.
They cried out in a loud voice, saying:
Salvation belongs to our God
who is seated on the throne,
and to the Lamb.   —Revelation 7:9-10

Let us give thanks for these brothers and sisters in Christ
to whom God has granted rest from their labors.

A list of names may be read.

Almighty God, we give you thanks
for these your servants
whom we remember today.
Grant us grace to follow them as they followed Christ.
Bring us, with them, to those things no eye has seen,
nor ear heard, which you have prepared
for those who love you.

Give us faith to look beyond touch and sight,
and seeing that we are surrounded
by so great a cloud of witnesses,
enable us to run with perseverance
the race that is set before us,
looking to Jesus, the author and finisher of our faith.   —Hebrews 12:1-2

Bring us at last to your eternal peace,
through Jesus Christ, our Lord. Amen.

195   For All The Saints Who Showed Your Love

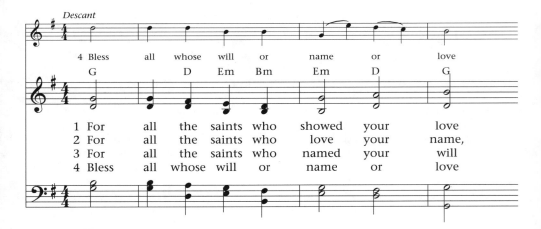

Descant

4 Bless all whose will or name or love

1 For all the saints who showed your love
2 For all the saints who love your name,
3 For all the saints who named your will
4 Bless all whose will or name or love

Text: John Bell (b. 1949)
Music: Louis Bourgeois (1510-1561); desc. Randall DeBruyn (b. 1947)
Text © 1989, 1996, WGRG the Iona Community (Scotland), admin. GIA Publications, Inc.; desc. © 1982, OCP Publications

LM
OLD HUNDREDTH

196 Our Father in Heaven

Our Fa - ther in heaven, hal - lowed be your name.

Your king - dom come. Your will be done, on earth as in heaven.

Give us to - day our dai - ly bread. For - give us our sins

as we for - give those who sin a - gainst us.

Save us from the time of trial, and de - liv - er us from e - vil.

Text: Matthew 6:9-13; tr. English Language Liturgical Consultation (1998)
Music: Nicholas Rimsky-Korsakov (1844-1908); arr. George Black (b. 1931)

Arr. © George Black

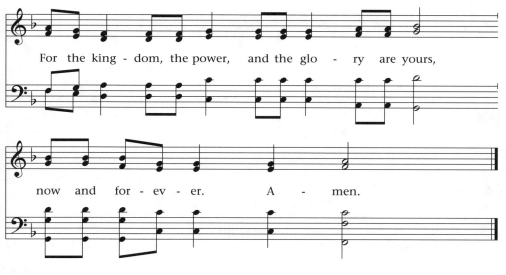

For the king - dom, the power, and the glo - ry are yours,

now and for - ev - er. A - men.

Ask, Seek, and Knock

197

Ask, and it will be giv - en to you; seek, and you will

find it; knock, and the door will be o - pened for

you; the Lord will an - swer your prayers.

Text and music: Mark Barnard (b. 1959), based on Matthew 7:7
© 1997, Lorenz Publishing Co.

198   Mayenziwe / Your Will Be Done

Text: from the Lord's Prayer
Music: South African traditional, as taught by George Mxadana; arr. John Bell (b. 1949)

Psalm 25

Refrain

To you, O Lord, I lift my soul,

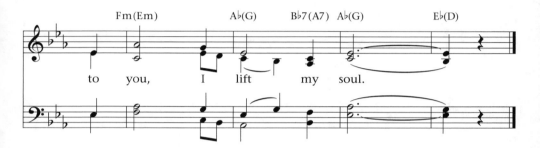

to you, I lift my soul.

Refrain

¹ To you, O LORD, I lift up my soul.
² O my God, in you I trust;
  do not let me be put to shame;
  do not let my enemies exult over me.
³ Do not let those who wait for you be put
    to shame;
  let them be ashamed who are wantonly
    treacherous.

Refrain

⁴ Make me to know your ways, O LORD;
  teach me your paths.
⁵ Lead me in your truth, and teach me,
  for you are the God of my salvation;
  for you I wait all day long.
⁶ Be mindful of your mercy, O LORD, and of
    your steadfast love,
  for they have been from of old.

⁷ Do not remember the sins of my youth or
    my transgressions;
  according to your steadfast love
    remember me,
  for your goodness' sake, O LORD!

Refrain

⁸ Good and upright is the LORD;
  therefore he instructs sinners in the
    way.
⁹ He leads the humble in what is right,
  and teaches the humble his way.
¹⁰ All the paths of the LORD are steadfast
    love and faithfulness,
  for those who keep his covenant and
    decrees.

Refrain

200 When the Storms of Life Are Raging

Capo 1

(A) Bb   (D) Eb   (Em/D) Fm/Eb   (D) Eb   (G) Ab   (D) Eb

1 When the storms of life are rag - ing, stand by me;
2 In the midst of trib - u - la - tion, stand by me;
3 In the midst of faults and fail - ures, stand by me;
4 In the midst of per - se - cu - tion, stand by me;
5 When I'm grow - ing old and fee - ble, stand by me;

(G/A) Ab/Bb   (D) Eb   (A/E) Bb/F   (D) Eb   (A) Bb

when the storms of life are rag - ing, stand by me.
in the midst of trib - u - la - tion, stand by me.
in the midst of faults and fail - ures, stand by me.
in the midst of per - se - cu - tion, stand by me.
when I'm grow - ing old and fee - ble, stand by me.

(A7) Bb7   (D) Eb   (Bm) Cm   (F#) G   (G) Ab

When the world is toss - ing me, like a ship up - on the sea,
When the host of hell as - sail, and my strength be - gins to fail,
When I've done the best I can, and my friends mis - un - der - stand,
When my foes in war ar - ray un - der - take to stop my way,
When my life be - comes a burden and I'm near - ing chil - ly Jordan,

Text and music: Charles Albert Tindley (1851-1933); arr. J. Jefferson Cleveland (1936-1986) and Verolga Nix (b. 1933)

STAND BY ME

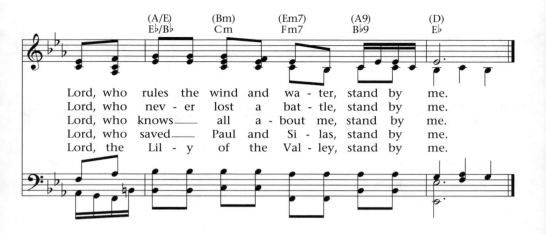

Lord, who rules the wind and wa-ter, stand by me.
Lord, who nev-er lost a bat-tle, stand by me.
Lord, who knows all a-bout me, stand by me.
Lord, who saved Paul and Si-las, stand by me.
Lord, the Lil-y of the Val-ley, stand by me.

Psalm 85   201

Sal-va-tion is com-ing near. Glo-ry is fill-ing our land.

Refrain

¹ LORD, you were favorable to your land;
  you restored the fortunes of Jacob.
² You forgave the iniquity of your people;
  you pardoned all their sin.
³ You withdrew all your wrath;
  you turned from your hot anger.

⁴ **Restore us again, O God of our salvation,**
  and put away your indignation toward us.
⁵ Will you be angry with us forever?
  Will you prolong your anger to all
    generations?
⁶ Will you not revive us again,
  so that your people may rejoice in you?
⁷ **Show us your steadfast love, O LORD,**
  and grant us your salvation.

Refrain

⁸ Let me hear what God the LORD will speak,
  for he will speak peace to his people,
  to his faithful, to those who turn to him
    in their hearts.
⁹ **Surely his salvation is at hand for those**
  who fear him,
    that his glory may dwell in our land.

¹⁰ Steadfast love and faithfulness will meet;
  righteousness and peace will kiss each
    other.
¹¹ **Faithfulness will spring up from the**
  ground,
    and righteousness will look down from
    the sky.
¹² The LORD will give what is good,
  and our land will yield its increase.
¹³ **Righteousness will go before him,**
  and will make a path for his steps.

Refrain

202   Let Us Pray to the Lord

In peace, let us pray to the Lord.
Lord, hear our prayer.

For the peace from above,
for the loving kindness of God,
and for our salvation,
let us pray to the Lord.
Lord, hear our prayer.

For the peace of the world,
for the unity of the church of God,
and for the well-being of all peoples,
let us pray to the Lord.
Lord, hear our prayer.

For this gathering of the faithful,
and for all who offer here
their worship and praise,
let us pray to the Lord.
Lord, hear our prayer.

For all the baptized,
for all who serve in the church,
[for N.],
let us pray to the Lord.
Lord, hear our prayer.

For our elected officials,
for the leaders of the nations,
and for all in authority,
let us pray to the Lord.
Lord, hear our prayer.

For this city (town, village, etc.),
for every city and community,
and for those who live in them,
let us pray to the Lord.
Lord, hear our prayer.

For seasonable weather,
and for abundant harvests for all to share,
let us pray to the Lord.
Lord, hear our prayer.

For the good earth which God has given us,
and for the wisdom and will to conserve it,
let us pray to the Lord.
Lord, hear our prayer.

For those who travel by land, water, or air
[or through outer space],
let us pray to the Lord.
Lord, hear our prayer.

For the aged and infirm,
for the widowed and orphaned,
and for the sick and the suffering,
let us pray to the Lord.
Lord, hear our prayer.

For the poor and the oppressed,
for those unemployed and the destitute,
for prisoners and captives,
and for all who remember and care for them,
let us pray to the Lord.
Lord, hear our prayer.

For deliverance in times of affliction,
strife, and need,
let us pray to the Lord.
Lord, hear our prayer.

Other petitions may be added. After a brief
silence, the leader concludes the prayers with the
following prayer, or another chosen prayer. This
prayer may be spoken, even though the litany
itself is sung.

Text: from the Eastern liturgies of St. Basil and St. John Chrysostom
Music: Byzantine chant

Almighty God,
you have given us grace at this time with
    one accord
to make our common supplication to you;
and you have promised through your
    beloved Son
that when two or three are gathered
    together in his name
you will be in the midst of them.

Fulfill now, O Lord, our desires and
    petitions as may be best for us,
granting us in this world
    knowledge of your truth,
and in the age to come
    life everlasting.
Amen.

O Lord, Hear My Prayer 203

Text: Psalm 102:1-2; adapt. The Community of Taizé
Music: Jacques Berthier (1923-1994)

© 1991, Les Presses de Taizé (France), admin. GIA Publications, Inc.

204 Lord, Make Us Servants

5 Dy - ing, we live, re - born through

D   G   C   Gsus   G   Bm

1 Lord, make us ser - vants of your peace: where there is
2 Where all is doubt, may we sow faith; where all is
3 Je - sus, our Lord, may we not seek to be con -
4 May we not look for love's re - turn, but seek to
5 Dy - ing, we live, and are re - born through death's dark

night to end - less day; Lord, make us ser - vants of

Em   Am   G   Dsus   D   G   C

hate, may we sow love; where there is hurt, may we for -
gloom, may we sow hope; where all is night, may we sow
soled, but to con - sole, nor look to un - der - stand - ing
love un - self - ish - ly, for in our giv - ing we re -
night to end - less day; Lord, make us ser - vants of Your

Text: James Quinn (b. 1919), after a prayer attr. to Francis of Assisi (1182-1226)
Music: English folk melody; arr. Hal H. Hopson (b. 1933); desc. Emily R. Brink (b. 1940)

LM
O WALY WALY

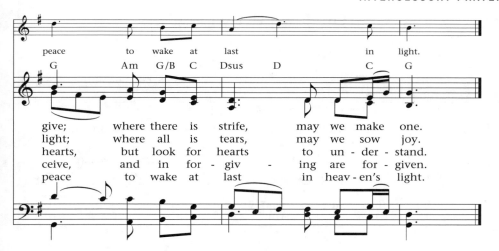

peace to wake at last in light.

give; where there is strife, may we make one.
light; where all is tears, may we sow joy.
hearts, but look for hearts to un-der-stand.
ceive, and in for-giv-ing are for-given.
peace to wake at last in heav-en's light.

Healer of Our Every Ill 205

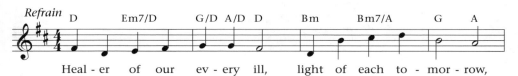

Heal-er of our ev-ery ill, light of each to-mor-row,

give us peace be-yond our fear and hope be-yond our sor-row.

1 You who know our fears and sad-ness, grace us with your
2 In the pain and joy be-hold-ing, how your grace is
3 Give us strength to love each oth-er, ev-ery sis-ter,
4 You who know each thought and feel-ing, teach us all your

peace and glad-ness. Spir-it of all com-fort, fill our hearts.
still un-fold-ing. Give us all your vis-ion, God of love.
ev-ery broth-er. Spir-it of all kind-ness, be our guide.
way of heal-ing. Spir-it of com-pas-sion, fill each heart.

Text and music: Marty Haugen (b. 1950)   HEALER (HAUGEN)

206   The Lord Is My Light

Refrain
Capo 3

The Lord is my light and my sal-va-tion, of whom should I
be a-fraid, of whom should I be a-fraid?

Refrain

O God, who is light in the darkness,
  we pray for those among us
  who in the night hours work their shifts,
  or those who labor in places where light is
  dim.
Be for them and for us protection in the
  dark.

O God, who is the bright Morning Star,
  we pray for those among us who grieve
the loss of loved ones,
the tarnishing of innocence,
the failing of health,
the flight of security.
Be for them and for us a sure defense
and the promise of a new day.

Refrain

O God, who is sight to the blind,
  we pray for those among us
whose eyes are clouded,

who are blind in soul, mind, or body.
Be for them and for us both courage and
  sight.

O God, who is strength to the besieged,
  we pray for those among us who are
    beset by temptation,
  those who are in danger,
those whose enemies are close and whose
    help seems far away.
Be for them and for us a present fortress
  against our foes.

Refrain

O God, who is salvation to the lost,
  we pray for those among us who have
    never found your way,
  or who, having found it,
  have strayed from your path.
Be for them and for us the beacon that
  guides safely home.

Refrain

Refrain text: Psalm 27:1
Music: David Haas (b. 1957)
Prayer: Kathleen Hart Brumm (b. 1958)

O God, who is comfort to the fearful,
  we pray for those among us
  who live in fear of threats real or
    imagined,
  whose lives are torn by war,
  whose thoughts are confused by mental
    illness,
  whose souls and bodies are ravaged by
    abuse.
**Be for them and for us consolation and
surety against anxiety.**

Refrain

Give us wisdom, O God, to turn to you in
  times of stress, fear and grief,
  in times of blindness, temptation, danger
  and perdition.
**Grant us patience to wait for you,
and courage to be strong in your might,
through Jesus Christ, our Lord. Amen.**

We Pray for Peace

207

Text and music: Ken Medema (b. 1943)
© 1993, Ken Medema Music/Brier Patch Music

208   I Lift My Eyes Up

Text and music: Brian Doerksen (b. 1965)

Ososo / Come Now, O Prince of Peace

209

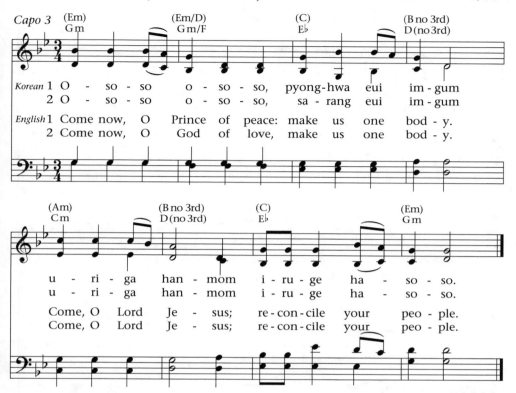

3 Ososo ososo,
chayu eui imgum,
uriga hanmom
iruge ha soso.

3 Come now and set us free,
O God our Savior.
Come, O Lord Jesus;
reconcile all nations.

4 Ososo ososo
tongil eui imgum,
uriga hanmom
iruge hasoso.

4 Come, Hope of unity;
make us one body.
Come, O Lord Jesus;
reconcile all nations.

Text and music: Geonyong Lee (b. 1947); para. Marion Pope (b. 1928)

65 56
O-SO-SO

210 Psalm 126: When God First Brought Us Back from Exile

1 When God first brought us back from exile, we were as dazed as those who dream. Then were our mouths brimming with laughter; joy from our lips gushed like a stream. The god-less cried in envious wonder, "Look what the Lord has done for them!" Indeed our God has greatly blessed us; rejoice and sing, Jerusalem!

2 Once more, O Lord, restore your people; come with your saving help again, as to the brookbeds in the desert you bring the sweet, reviving rain. Let those who sow with tears and sighing sing as they reap when seed is scattered; gather their sheaves and praise your name. may those who weep and joy proclaim:

Text: Carl P. Daw, Jr. (b. 1944)
Music: Traditional American
Text © 1996, Hope Publishing Co.

98 98 D
WAYFARING STRANGER

"Abba, Abba, Hear Us," We Cry

1 "Ab - ba, Ab - ba, hear us," we cry; God's Spir - it
2 With the whole cre - a - tion we cry, groan as in
3 As we pray, the Spir - it breathes sighs, sighs far too

cries in us and pro - claims us slaves no more, but
child - birth. Soon all sin, all death will be no
deep for words; and the God who search - es ev - ery

heirs, the heirs of God. All cre - a - tion
more; we shall be free. All cre - a - tion
heart hears all our prayer. All cre - a - tion

waits, ea - ger and long - ing; soon God's child - ren,
waits, ea - ger and long - ing; for the glo - rious
waits, ea - ger and long - ing; pa - tient - ly we

glo - rious and free, will be re - vealed.
prom - ise of God we wait and pray.
wait, for in all God works for good.

Text: Andrew Donaldson (b. 1951), based on Romans 8
Music: Korean traditional

212 Spirit Song

D   Gmaj7   A9/G   F#m7

1 O let the Son of God en - fold you with his Spir - it and his
2 O come and sing this song with glad-ness as your hearts are filled with

Bm7   Em7   A7   Dmaj7

love; let him fill your heart and sat - is - fy your soul.
joy; lift your hands in sweet sur - ren-der to his name.

C/D D7 Gmaj7   A9/G   F#m7

O let him have the things that hold you, and the Spir - it like a
O give him all your tears and sad-ness; give him all your years of

Bm7   Em7   A7   D   C/D D7

dove will de - scend up-on your life and make you whole.
pain, and you'll en - ter in - to life in Je - sus' name.

Text and music: John Wimber (1934-1997)
© 1979 Mercy/Vineyard Publishing, admin. Music Services

SPIRIT SONG

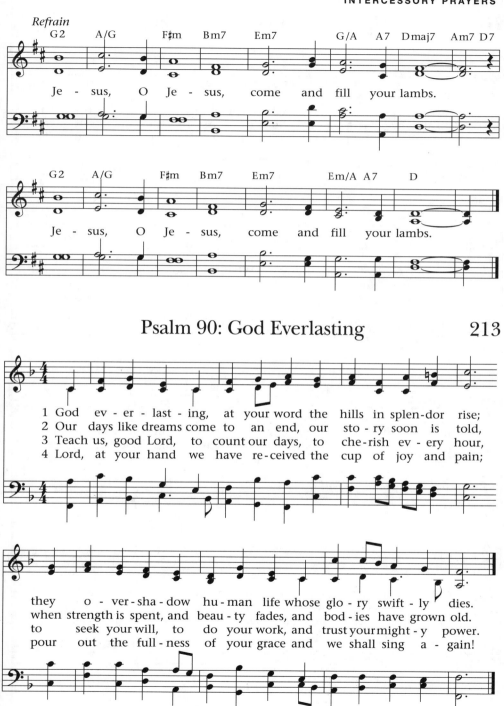

Refrain

Je - sus, O Je - sus, come and fill your lambs.

Je - sus, O Je - sus, come and fill your lambs.

Psalm 90: God Everlasting 213

1 God ev-er-last-ing, at your word the hills in splen-dor rise;
2 Our days like dreams come to an end, our sto-ry soon is told,
3 Teach us, good Lord, to count our days, to che-rish ev-ery hour,
4 Lord, at your hand we have re-ceived the cup of joy and pain;

they o-ver-sha-dow hu-man life whose glo-ry swift-ly dies.
when strength is spent, and beau-ty fades, and bod-ies have grown old.
to seek your will, to do your work, and trust your might-y power.
pour out the full-ness of your grace and we shall sing a-gain!

Text: Psalm 90; para. David Mowbray (b. 1938)
Music: Jeremiah Clarke (1660-1707)

CM
ST. MAGNUS

214   Have We Any Gift Worth Giving

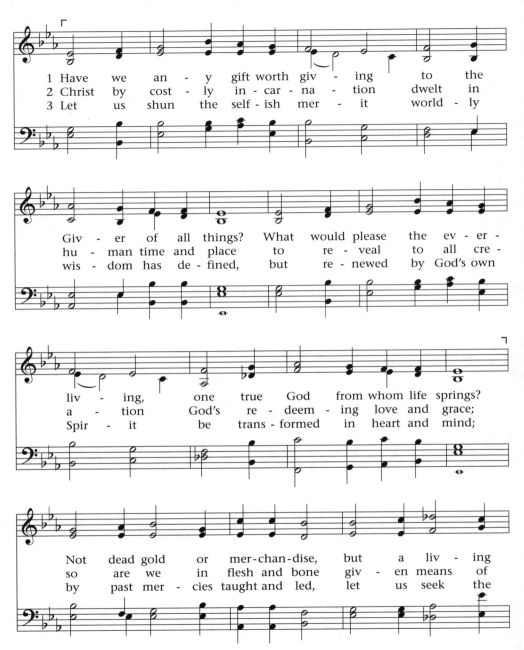

1 Have we an - y gift worth giv - ing to the
2 Christ by cost - ly in - car - na - tion dwelt in
3 Let us shun the self - ish mer - it world - ly

Giv - er of all things? What would please the ev - er -
hu - man time and place to re - veal to all cre -
wis - dom has de - fined, but re - newed by God's own

liv - ing, one true God from whom life springs?
a - tion God's re - deem - ing love and grace;
Spir - it be trans - formed in heart and mind;

Not dead gold or mer - chan - dise, but a liv - ing
so are we in flesh and bone giv - en means of
by past mer - cies taught and led, let us seek the

Text: Carl P. Daw, Jr. (b. 1944), based on Romans 12:1
Music: Alfred V. Fedak (b. 1953)

87 87 77 88
COSTLY GIFTS

sac - ri - fice: wor - ship both pro - found and free - ing,
mak - ing known through the web of dai - ly liv - ing
path a - head, trust - ing that, like those be - fore us,

serv - ing God with all our be - ing.
God's own pat - tern of self - giv - ing.
God will guide us and re - store us.

Take, O Take Me As I Am 215

Take, O take me as I am; sum - mon out what I shall be;

set your seal up - on my heart and live in me.

Text and music: John Bell (b. 1949)

216

Give Thanks

Give thanks with a grate-ful heart, give thanks to the Ho-ly One; give thanks be-cause he's giv-en Je - sus Christ, his Son. Give Son. And now let the weak say, "We are strong!" let the poor say, "We are rich be-cause of

Text and music: Henry Smith (b. 1952)

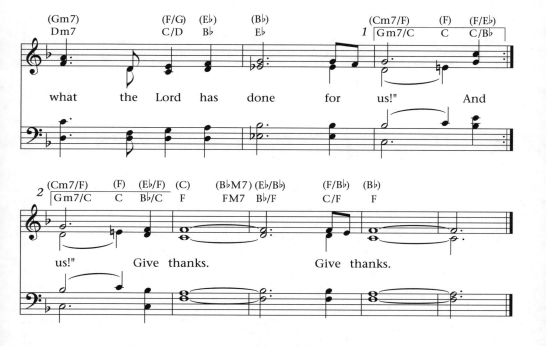

Prayer at the Presentation of the Offering   217

We bring our gifts to you, Lord God,
with cheerfulness and a joyful heart.
Grant that with our gifts
we may also offer
a ready mind and a willing spirit
to show forth in our lives
the truth of the gospel;
through Jesus Christ our Lord.
Amen.

218   I Offer My Life

1 All that I am, all that I have, I lay them down
2 Things in the past, things yet un-seen, wish-es and dreams

be - fore you,—— O Lord; all my re - grets,
that are yet to come true; all of my hopes,

all my ac-claim, the joy and the pain, I'm mak - ing them yours.
all of my plans, my heart and my hands are lift - ed to you.

Refrain

Lord, I of-fer my life to you, ev - 'ry-thing I've

been through, use it for your glo - ry. Lord, I of-fer my days

to you, lift-ing my praise to you as a pleas-ing sac-ri-fice.

Lord, I of-fer you my life. life.

Text and music: Claire Cloninger (b. 1942) and Don Moen (b. 1950)

2 Am9 · Cmaj7/D · D · Bm11 · D/E · Em

life. 3 What can we give that you have not giv - en; and

Am9 · D · Bm7 · Em · Am9 · D

what do we have that is not al-read-y yours? All we pos-sess are these lives

Bm7 · D/E · E · Am7 · G/B · A/B · *Refrain*

we're liv - ing, and that's what we give to you, Lord.

Gracias, Señor / We Give You Thanks 219

Capo 1

(D) Eb · (E) F · (A) Bb · (D) Eb · (E) F · (A) Bb · (D) Eb

Spanish ¡Gra - cias, Se - ñor! ¡Gra - cias, Se - ñor! Por tu bon-y

English We give you thanks. We give you praise. For you are

(C#7) D7 · (F#m) Gm · (Bm7(b5)/D) Cm7(b5)/Eb · (A/E) Bb/F · (Esus) F7sus · (E7) F7 · (A) Bb

dad, tu po - der, por tu a-mor; ¡Gra - cias, Se - ñor!

kind, you are love, you are God! We give you thanks.

Text and music: Jorge A. Lockward (b. 1965)

© 1996, 2000, Abingdon Press, admin. The Copyright Company

LOCKWARD

220 In the Lord I'll Be Ever Thankful

English In the Lord I'll be ev-er thank-ful, in the Lord I will re-joice!
Spanish El Se-ñor es la nue-va fuer-za, el Se-ñor es mi can-tor.

Look to God, do not be a-fraid. Lift up your voic-es, the Lord is
En él es-tá la sal-va-ción. En él con-fí-o, no te-me-

near; lift up your voic-es, the Lord is near. In the
ré. En él con-fí-o, no tem-e-ré. El Se-

Text: The Community of Taizé; Sp. tr. Alejandro Pimentel (b. 1960)
Music: Jacques Berthier (1923-1994)

Psalm 30

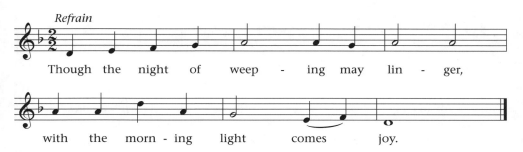

Though the night of weep - ing may lin - ger,

with the morn - ing light comes joy.

Refrain

1 I will extol you, O LORD, for you have
    drawn me up,
    and did not let my foes rejoice over me.
2 **O LORD my God, I cried to you for help,**
    and you have healed me.
3 **O LORD, you brought up my soul from**
    Sheol,
    restored me to life from among those
    gone down to the Pit.
4 Sing praises to the LORD, O you his faithful
    ones,
    and give thanks to his holy name.
5 **For his anger is but for a moment;**
    his favor is for a lifetime.
    Weeping may linger for the night,
    but joy comes with the morning.

Refrain

6 As for me, I said in my prosperity,
    "I shall never be moved."
7 **By your favor, O LORD,**
    you had established me as a strong
    mountain;
    you hid your face;
    I was dismayed.

8 To you, O LORD, I cried,
    and to the LORD I made supplication:
9 **"What profit is there in my death,**
    if I go down to the Pit?
    Will the dust praise you?
    Will it tell of your faithfulness?
10 **Hear, O LORD, and be gracious to me!**
    O LORD, be my helper!"

Refrain

11 You have turned my mourning into
    dancing;
    you have taken off my sackcloth
    and clothed me with joy,
12 so that my soul may praise you and not be
    silent.
    O LORD my God, I will give thanks to
    you forever.

Refrain

Refrain text: Psalm 30:5
Music: French, 17th cent.

PICAROY

222   Psalm 65

Shout to the Lord, all the earth. Let us sing.

[1] Praise is due to you,
  O God, in Zion;
and to you shall vows be performed,
[2] O you who answer prayer!
To you all flesh shall come.
[3] **When deeds of iniquity overwhelm us,
  you forgive our transgressions.**
[4] Happy are those whom you choose and
    bring near
  to live in your courts.
We shall be satisfied with the goodness of
    your house,
  your holy temple.
[5] **By awesome deeds you answer us with
    deliverance,
  O God of our salvation;
you are the hope of all the ends of the
    earth
  and of the farthest seas.**
[6] By your strength you established the
    mountains;
  you are girded with might.
[7] You silence the roaring of the seas,
  the roaring of their waves,
  the tumult of the peoples.

[8] **Those who live at earth's farthest bounds
  are awed by your signs;
you make the gateways of the morning
  and the evening shout for joy.**

Refrain

[9] You visit the earth and water it,
  you greatly enrich it;
the river of God is full of water;
  you provide the people with grain,
  for so you have prepared it.
[10] You water its furrows abundantly,
  settling its ridges,
softening it with showers,
  and blessing its growth.
[11] **You crown the year with your bounty;
  your wagon tracks overflow with
    richness.**
[12] The pastures of the wilderness overflow,
  the hills gird themselves with joy,
[13] the meadows clothe themselves with
    flocks,
  the valleys deck themselves with grain,
  they shout and sing together for joy.

Refrain

223   Shout to the Lord

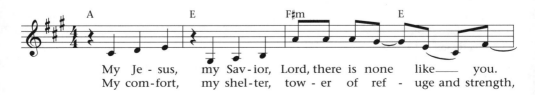

My Je - sus, my Sav - ior, Lord, there is none like—— you.
My com - fort, my shel - ter, tow - er of ref - uge and strength,

Text and music: Darlene Zschech (b. 1965)

224 Cantad al Señor / O Sing to the Lord

Spanish 1 Can - tad al Se - ñor un cán - ti - co nue - vo.
English 1 O sing to the Lord, O sing God a new song.

Can - tad al Se - ñor un cán - ti - co nue - vo.
O sing to the Lord, O sing God a new song.

Can - tad al Se - ñor un cán - ti - co nue - vo.
O sing to the Lord, O sing God a new song.

¡Can - tad al Se - ñor, can - tad al Se - ñor!
O sing to our God, O sing to our God.

2 Pues nuestro Señor
  ha hecho prodigios. *(3x)*
  ¡Cantad al Señor,
  cantad al Señor!

3 Cantad al Señor,
  alabadle con arpa. *(3x)*
  ¡Cantad al Señor,
  cantad al Señor!

4 Es él que nos da
  el Espíritu Santo. *(3x)*
  ¡Cantad al Señor,
  cantad al Señor!

5 ¡Jesus es Señor!
  ¡Amén, aleluya! *(3x)*
  ¡Cantad al Señor,
  cantad al Señor!

2 For God is the Lord, and
  God has done wonders. *(3x)*
  O sing to our God,
  O sing to our God.

3 So dance for our God
  and blow all the trumpets. *(3x)*
  O sing to our God,
  O sing to our God.

4 O shout to our God,
  who gave us the Spirit. *(3x)*
  O sing to our God,
  O sing to our God.

5 For Jesus is Lord!
  Amen! Alleluia! *(3x)*
  O sing to our God,
  O sing to our God.

Text and music: Brazilian (Portuguese) folk hymn; Sp. and Eng. tr. Gerhard M. Cartford (b. 1924)
Tr. © Gerhard M. Cartford

CANTAD AL SENOR

Psalm 66

Refrain *(sing 224, st. 1)*

1 Make a joyful noise to God, all the earth;
2   sing the glory of his name;
   give to him glorious praise.
3 Say to God, **"How awesome are your deeds!**
   Because of your great power, your enemies cringe before you.
4 **All the earth worships you;**
   they sing praises to you,
   sing praises to your name."

Refrain *(st. 2)*

5 Come and see what God has done:
   he is awesome in his deeds among mortals.
6a He turned the sea into dry land;
   they passed through the river on foot.
8 **Bless our God, O peoples,**
   let the sound of his praise be heard,
9 **who has kept us among the living,**
   and has not let our feet slip.

Refrain *(st. 3)*

10 For you, O God, have tested us;
   you have tried us as silver is tried.
11 You brought us into the net;
   you laid burdens on our backs;
12 you let people ride over our heads;
   we went through fire and through water;
   yet you have brought us out to a spacious place.

Refrain (st. 4)

16   Come and hear, all you who fear God,
   and I will tell you what God has done for me.
17   I cried aloud to him,
    and he was extolled with my tongue.
18 **If I had cherished iniquity in my heart,**
   the Lord would not have listened.
19 **But truly God has listened;**
   he has given heed to the words of my prayer.
20 Blessed be God,
   because he has not rejected my prayer
   or removed his steadfast love from me.

Refrain (st. 5)

226

Psalm 116

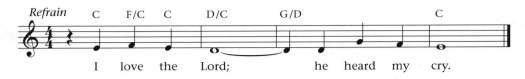

Refrain

I love the Lord; he heard my cry.

Refrain

1 I love the LORD, because he has heard
   my voice and my supplications.
2 **Because he inclined his ear to me,**
   therefore I will call on him as long as I
   live.
3 The snares of death encompassed me;
   the pangs of Sheol laid hold on me;
   I suffered distress and anguish.
4 **Then I called on the name of the LORD:**
   "O LORD, I pray, save my life!"
5 Gracious is the LORD, and righteous;
   our God is merciful.
6 **The LORD protects the simple;**
   when I was brought low, he saved me.
7 Return, O my soul, to your rest,
   for the LORD has dealt bountifully with
   you.
8 For you have delivered my soul from
   death,
   my eyes from tears,
   my feet from stumbling.

Refrain

9 I walk before the LORD
   in the land of the living.
10 **I kept my faith, even when I said,**
   "I am greatly afflicted";
11 **I said in my consternation,**
   "Everyone is a liar."

12 What shall I return to the LORD
   for all his bounty to me?
13 **I will lift up the cup of salvation**
   and call on the name of the LORD,
14 **I will pay my vows to the LORD**
   in the presence of all his people.

Refrain

15 Precious in the sight of the LORD
   is the death of his faithful ones.
16 **O LORD, I am your servant;**
   I am your servant, the child of your
   serving girl.
   You have loosed my bonds.
17 I will offer to you a thanksgiving
   sacrifice
   and call on the name of the LORD.
18 **I will pay my vows to the LORD**
   in the presence of all his people,
19 **in the courts of the house of the LORD,**
   in your midst, O Jerusalem.
Praise the LORD!

Refrain

Refrain: African-American spiritual

I Love the Lord

Text: Psalm 116:1-2; vers. Isaac Watts (1674-1748)
Music: African-American spiritual; harm. Richard Smallwood (b. 1948)

228 Psalm 107

Refrain

Now thank we all our God with heart and hands and voic - es.

Refrain

1 O give thanks to the LORD, for he is good;
for his steadfast love endures forever.
2 **Let the redeemed of the LORD say so,**
those he redeemed from trouble
3 **and gathered in from the lands,**
from the east and from the west,
from the north and from the south.

Refrain

4 Some wandered in desert wastes,
finding no way to an inhabited town;
5 hungry and thirsty,
their soul fainted within them.
6 **Then they cried to the LORD in their**
trouble,
and he delivered them from their
distress;
7 **he led them by a straight way,**
until they reached an inhabited town.
8 Let them thank the LORD for his steadfast
love,
for his wonderful works to humankind.
9 **For he satisfies the thirsty,**
and the hungry he fills with good things.

Refrain

17 Some were sick through their sinful ways,
and because of their iniquities endured
affliction;
18 they loathed any kind of food,
and they drew near to the gates of death.
19 **Then they cried to the LORD in their**
trouble,
and he saved them from their distress;
20 **he sent out his word and healed them,**
and delivered them from destruction.

21 Let them thank the LORD for his steadfast
love,
for his wonderful works to humankind.
22 **And let them offer thanksgiving sacrifices,**
and tell of his deeds with songs of joy.

Refrain

23 Some went down to the sea in ships,
doing business on the mighty waters;
24 they saw the deeds of the LORD,
his wondrous works in the deep.
25 **For he commanded and raised the stormy**
wind,
which lifted up the waves of the sea.
26 They mounted up to heaven, they went
down to the depths;
their courage melted away in their
calamity;
27 they reeled and staggered like drunkards,
and were at their wits' end.
28 **Then they cried to the LORD in their**
trouble,
and he brought them out from their
distress;
29 **he made the storm be still,**
and the waves of the sea were hushed.
30 **Then they were glad because they had quiet,**
and he brought them to their desired
haven.
31 Let them thank the LORD for his steadfast
love,
for his wonderful works to humankind.
32 **Let them extol him in the congregation of**
the people,
and praise him in the assembly of the
elders.

Refrain

Refrain text: Martin Rinkart (1586-1649); tr. Catherine Winkworth (1827-1878)
Music: Johann Crüger (1598-1662)

NUN DANKET

Psalm 138

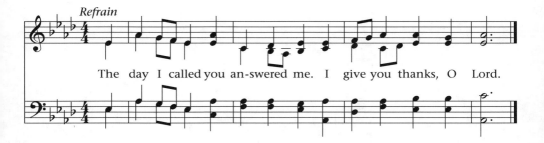

The day I called you an-swered me. I give you thanks, O Lord.

Refrain

¹ I give you thanks, O LORD, with my whole heart;
  before the gods I sing your praise;
² I bow down toward your holy temple
    and give thanks to your name for your steadfast love and your
      faithfulness;
    for you have exalted your name and your word
    above everything.
³ **On the day I called, you answered me,**
    you increased my strength of soul.

Refrain

⁴ All the kings of the earth shall praise you, O LORD,
  for they have heard the words of your mouth.
⁵ **They shall sing of the ways of the LORD,**
  for great is the glory of the LORD.
⁶ For though the LORD is high, he regards the lowly;
  but the haughty he perceives from far away.

Refrain

⁷ Though I walk in the midst of trouble,
  you preserve me against the wrath of my enemies;
you stretch out your hand,
  and your right hand delivers me.
⁸ The LORD will fulfill his purpose for me;
    your steadfast love, O LORD, endures forever.
    Do not forsake the work of your hands.

Refrain

Refrain text: from Ps. 138:1, 3
Music: *Gesangbuch*, Wittenberg (1784)

ELLACOMBE

230 We Are an Offering

Text and music: Dwight Liles (b. 1957)

© 1984, Word Music, Inc.

OFFERING

A Living Sacrifice

231

I appeal to you therefore, brothers and sisters,
by the mercies of God,
to present your bodies as a living sacrifice,
holy and acceptable to God,
which is your spiritual worship.

—Romans 12:1

Be imitators of God, as beloved children.

—Ephesians 5:1

We present our bodies as a living sacrifice.

Live in love as Christ loved you.

We present our bodies as a living sacrifice.

Be imitators of Christ
who gave himself up for us,
a fragrant offering and sacrifice to God.

—Ephesians 5:2

We present our bodies as a living sacrifice.

The grace of our Lord Jesus Christ, the love of God,
and the communion of the Holy Spirit be with you all.
And also with you.

232 What Gift Can We Bring

1 What gift can we bring, what pres - ent, what to - ken?
2 Give thanks for the past, for those who had vi - sion,
3 Give thanks for to - mor - row, full of sur - pris - es,
4 This gift we now bring, this pres - ent, this to - ken,

What words can con - vey it, the joy of this day?
who plant - ed and wa - tered so dreams could come true.
for know - ing what - ev - er to - mor - row may bring,
these words can't con - vey it, the joy of this day!

When grate - ful we come, re - mem - bering, re - joic - ing,
Give thanks for the now, for stud - y, for wor - ship,
the Word is our prom - ise al - ways, for - ev - er;
when grate - ful we come, re - mem - bering, re - joic - ing,

what song can we of - fer in hon - or and praise?
for mis - sion that bids us turn prayer in - to deed.
we rest in God's keep - ing and live in God's love.
this song we now of - fer in hon - or and praise!

Text and music: Jane Marshall (b. 1924)
© 1982, Hope Publishing Co.

11 11 11 11
ANNIVERSARY SONG

Jonah's Song

233

1 In my trou - ble, in my trou - ble I cried out to the
2 I was sink - ing, I was sink - ing in dark - ness to the
3 Those who wor - ship worth - less i - dols will nev - er know the

Lord, my God, and,
o - cean floor, and, Lord, you heard me,
grace of God, but,

yes, you heard me; from the depths you heard my cry.

Though the wa - ter swirled a - round me, though the
When my prayer came to your tem - ple, you stretched
With a song of high thanks - giv - ing I will

deep waves thun - dered o'er me,
out your might - y hand.___ Lord, you saved me,
sac - ri - fice to God.___

yes, you saved me. You would not let your ser - vant die.

Text: Edith Bajema (b. 1952)
Music: Vicki Williams (b. 1962)

234 Come to the Water

Text and music: John Foley (b. 1939), based on Isaiah 55:1-2; Matthew 11:28-30

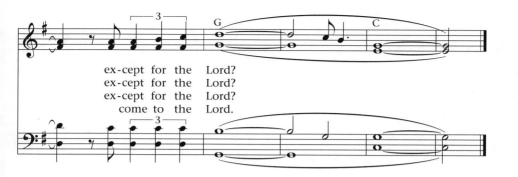

ex-cept for the Lord?
ex-cept for the Lord?
ex-cept for the Lord?
come to the Lord.

Loving Spirit 235

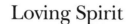

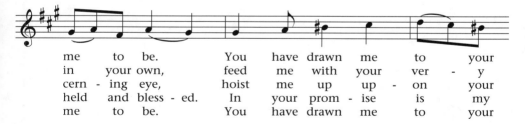

1 Lov - ing Spir - it, lov - ing Spir - it, you have cho - sen
2 Like a moth - er, you en - fold me, hold my life with -
3 Like a fa - ther, you pro - tect me, teach me the dis -
4 Friend and lov - er, in your close-ness I am known and
5 Lov - ing Spir - it, lov - ing Spir - it, you have cho - sen

me to be. You have drawn me to your
in your own, feed me with your ver - y
cern - ing eye, hoist me up up - on your
held and bless - ed. In your prom - ise is my
me to be. You have drawn me to your

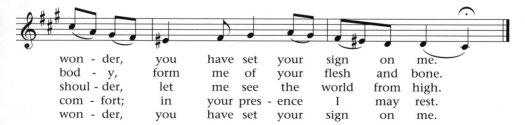

won - der, you have set your sign on me.
bod - y, form me of your flesh and bone.
shoul - der, let me see the world from high.
com - fort; in your pres - ence I may rest.
won - der, you have set your sign on me.

Text: Shirley Erena Murray (b. 1931)
Music: I-to Loh (b. 1936)
Alt. tune: ARISE, 237

87 87
CHHUN-BIN

236 Take Me to the Water

Text and music: African-American spiritual; arr. Horace Clarence Boyer (b. 1935)

© 1992, 2000, Horace Clarence Boyer

Crashing Waters at Creation

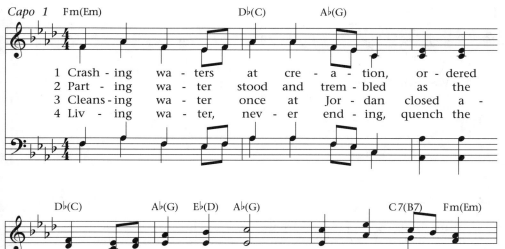

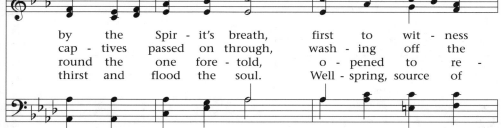

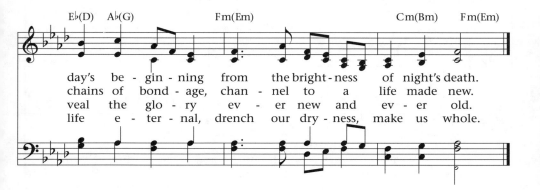

1 Crash - ing wa - ters at cre - a - tion, or - dered by the Spir - it's breath, first to wit - ness day's be - gin - ning from the bright - ness of night's death.

2 Part - ing wa - ter stood and trem - bled as the cap - tives passed on through, wash - ing off the chains of bond - age, chan - nel to a life made new.

3 Cleans - ing wa - ter once at Jor - dan closed a - round the one fore - told, o - pened to re - veal the glo - ry ev - er new and ev - er old.

4 Liv - ing wa - ter, nev - er end - ing, quench the thirst and flood the soul. Well - spring, source of life e - ter - nal, drench our dry - ness, make us whole.

Text: Sylvia G. Dunstan (1955-1993)
Music: W. Walker's *Southern Harmony* (1835)

Text © 1991, GIA Publications, Inc.

87 87
ARISE

238   Wash, O God, Our Sons and Daughters

1 Wash, O God, our sons and daugh - ters, where your cleans - ing wa - ters flow. Num - ber them a - mong your peo - ple; bless as Christ blessed long a - go. Weave them gar - ments bright and spark - ling; com - pass

2 We who bring them long for nur - ture; by your milk may we be fed. Let us join your feast, par - tak - ing cup of bless - ing, liv - ing bread. God, re - new us, guide our foot - steps, free from

3 Oh, how deep your ho - ly wis - dom! Un - im - ag - ined, all your ways! To your name be glo - ry, hon - or! With our lives we wor - ship, praise! We your peo - ple stand be - fore you, wa - ter -

Text: Ruth Duck (b. 1947)
Music: *The Sacred Harp*, 1844; arr. *Lutheran Book of Worship*

87 87 D
BEACH SPRING

them with love and light. Fill, a - noint them; send your
sin and all its snares, one with Christ in liv - ing,
washed and Spir - it - born. By your grace, our lives we

Spir - it, ho - ly dove and heart's de - light.
dy - ing, by your Spir - it, chil - dren, heirs.
of - fer. Re - cre - ate us: God, trans - form!

Wash Me Through and Through   239

Refrain

Wash me through and through, and cleanse me from my sin.

1 Wash me through the grace of God re - newed with - in
2 Wash me through the blood of Christ ap - plied with - in.
3 Wash me through the Spir - it's work a - live with - in.

Text: St. 1, Samuel Batt Owens (1928-1998); st. 2-3, Bert Polman (b. 1945)
Music: Samuel Batt Owens

Text (st. 1) and music © 1998, MorningStar Music Publishers; text (st. 2-3) © 2000, CRC Publications

240 Reaffirmation of Baptismal Vows

Brothers and sisters in Christ,
the promises of God's grace are signed and
    sealed to us in our baptism.
In baptism God promises by grace alone
to forgive our sins;
to adopt us into the body of Christ, the
    church;
to send the Holy Spirit daily to renew and
    cleanse us;
and to resurrect us to eternal life.

This promise is made visible in the water of
    baptism.

*(Here water is poured visibly and audibly into
the font.)*

Water cleanses, purifies, refreshes, sustains;
Jesus Christ is living water.

Through baptism Christ calls us to new
    obedience:
to love and trust God completely;
to forsake the evil of the world; and
to live a new and holy life.

I invite you now
to remember God's promise,
to turn away from all that is evil,
and to reaffirm your faith in Jesus Christ
and your commitment to Christ's church.

*(The people may stand and encircle the font.
When people are in place, the leader continues.)*

Renunciations and Affirmation

Trusting in the gracious promises of God,
do you renounce sin and the power of evil
in your life and in the world?
I renounce them.

Who is your Lord and Savior?
Jesus Christ is my Lord and Savior.

Will you be Christ's faithful disciple,
obeying his Word and showing his love?
God being my helper, I will.

Do you believe in God the Father?
**I believe in God the Father almighty,
creator of heaven and earth.**

Do you believe in Jesus Christ, the Son of
    God?
**I believe in Jesus Christ, God's only Son,
our Lord,
who was conceived by the Holy Spirit,
born of the Virgin Mary,
suffered under Pontius Pilate,
was crucified, died, and was buried.
He descended to the dead.
On the third day he rose again;
he ascended into heaven,
he is seated at the right hand of the Father,
and he will come to judge the living and the
dead.**

Do you believe in God the Holy Spirit?
**I believe in the Holy Spirit,
the holy catholic Church,
the communion of saints,
the forgiveness of sins,
the resurrection of the body,
and the life everlasting.**

The Prayers of the People
The Lord be with you.
And also with you.
Let us give thanks to the Lord our God.
It is right to give our thanks and praise.

We give you thanks, O holy and gracious
    God, for the gift of water.
In the beginning of creation your Spirit
    moved over the waters.
In the waters of the flood you destroyed evil.

You led the children of Israel through the
    sea
into the freedom of the promised land.
In the river Jordan, John baptized our Lord
and your Spirit anointed him.
By his death and resurrection Jesus Christ,
    the living water,
frees us from sin and death and opens the
    way to life everlasting.

All say or sing:

We have put on Christ, in him we have been bap - tized.

Al - le - lu - ia! Al - le - lu - ia!

Text: Galatians 3:27
Music: Howard Hughes (b. 1930)

BAPTIZED IN CHRIST

We thank you, O God, for the gift of baptism.
In the waters of baptism you confirm to us
that we are buried with Christ in his death,
raised to share in his resurrection,
and are being renewed by the Holy Spirit.

**We have put on Christ. In him we have
 been baptized. Alleluia! Alleluia!**

Pour out upon us and on your whole
 church the gift of your Holy Spirit,
so that all who have passed through the
 waters of baptism
might be dead to sin and alive to God in
 Christ Jesus.

**We have put on Christ. In him we have
 been baptized. Alleluia! Alleluia!**

To God be all honor and glory, dominion
 and power, now and forever,
through Jesus Christ our Lord, in whose
 name we are bold to pray:

**Our Father in heaven,
hallowed be your name,
your kingdom come,
your will be done,
on earth as in heaven.**

**Give us today our daily bread.
Forgive us our sins
as we forgive those who sin against us.
Save us from the time of trial
and deliver us from evil.
For the kingdom, the power, and the glory
 are yours
now and forever. Amen.**

Charge and Blessing

Lead a life worthy of the calling to which
 you have been called,
with humility and gentleness,
with patience, bearing with one another in
 love,
making every effort to maintain the unity
 of the Spirit
in the bond of peace.   —Ephesians 4:1-2

May the God of peace make you holy in
 every way
and may your whole being—spirit, soul,
 and body—
be kept sound and blameless
at the coming of our Lord Jesus Christ.

—1 Thessalonians 5:23

241 Sing! A New Creation

1 Sing! A new cre - a - tion calls us: God's Son,
2 Sing a - new! Cre - a - tion flow - ers as the
3 Sing a new cre - a - tion grow - ing life - trees

first - born from the dead, makes the drown - ing
Spir - it draws us near, safe from storm - ing,
by the Fath - er's stream. Go and teach, send

which be - falls us in - to cleans - ing birth in - stead.
earth-bound pow - ers on this ark, though tossed by fear.
jus - tice flow - ing, quench dry souls, com - pose a dream.

Text: James Hart Brumm (b. 1962)
Music: Thomas J. Williams (1869-1944)
Text © 2000, Wayne Leupold Editions, Inc.

87 87 D
EBENEZER

242   Psalm 105

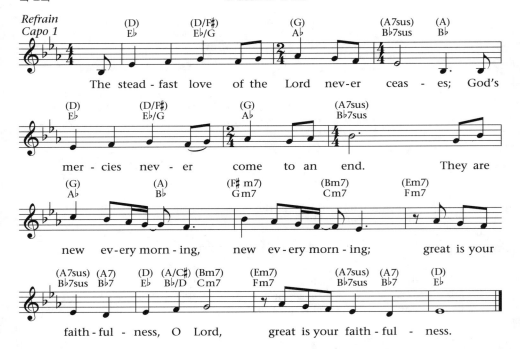

The stead-fast love of the Lord nev-er ceas - es; God's mer - cies nev - er come to an end. They are new ev-ery morn - ing, new ev - ery morn - ing; great is your faith - ful - ness, O Lord, great is your faith - ful - ness.

Refrain

¹ O give thanks to the LORD, call on his
    name,
    make known his deeds among the
    peoples.
² **Sing to him, sing praises to him;**
    tell of all his wonderful works.
³ Glory in his holy name;
    let the hearts of those who seek the
    LORD rejoice.
⁴ **Seek the LORD and his strength;**
    seek his presence continually.

Refrain

⁵ Remember the wonderful works he has
    done,
    his miracles, and the judgments he
    uttered,
⁶ O offspring of his servant Abraham,
    children of Jacob, his chosen ones.

⁷ **He is the LORD our God;**
    his judgments are in all the earth.
⁸ He is mindful of his covenant forever,
    of the word that he commanded, for a
    thousand generations,
⁹ **the covenant that he made with Abraham,**
    his sworn promise to Isaac,
¹⁰**which he confirmed to Jacob as a statute,**
    to Israel as an everlasting covenant.

Refrain

⁴²For he remembered his holy promise,
    and Abraham, his servant.
⁴³So he brought his people out with joy,
    his chosen ones with singing.
⁴⁴**He gave them the lands of the nations,**
    and they took possession of the wealth
    of the peoples,
⁴⁵**that they might keep his statutes**
    and observe his laws.
    Praise the LORD!

Refrain

Psalm 139: O Lord, My God

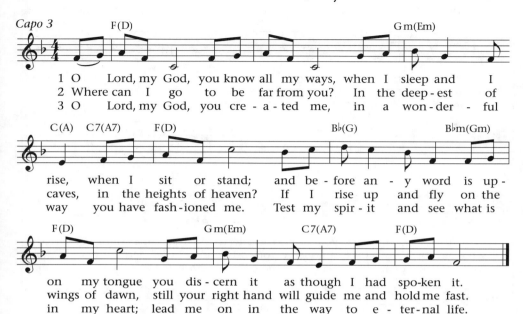

Capo 3

1 O Lord, my God, you know all my ways, when I sleep and I
2 Where can I go to be far from you? In the deep-est of
3 O Lord, my God, you cre-a-ted me, in a won-der-ful

rise, when I sit or stand; and be-fore an-y word is up-
caves, in the heights of heaven? If I rise up and fly on the
way you have fash-ioned me. Test my spir-it and see what is

on my tongue you dis-cern it as though I had spo-ken it.
wings of dawn, still your right hand will guide me and hold me fast.
in my heart; lead me on in the way to e-ter-nal life.

Text: Paul Wigmore (b. 1925)
Music: John Barnard (b. 1948)

SHEPHERDSWELL

© 1994, Jubilate Hymns Ltd., admin. Hope Publishing Co.

You Have Put on Christ

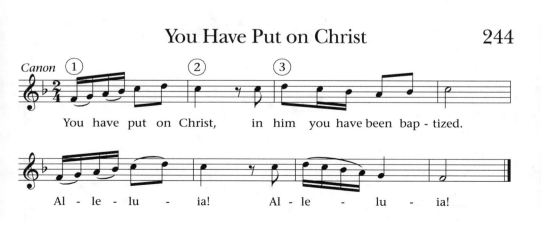

Canon

You have put on Christ, in him you have been bap-tized.

Al - le - lu - ia! Al - le - lu - ia!

Text: Galatians 3:27
Music: Howard Hughes (b. 1930)

© 1969, 1977, International Commission on English in the Liturgy

245   As We Gather at Your Table

Capo 3

1 As we gath-er at your Ta-ble, as we lis-ten to your Word,
2 Turn our wor-ship in-to wit-ness in the sac-ra-ment of life;
3 Gra-cious Spir-it, help us sum-mon oth-er guests to share that feast

help us know, O God, your pres-ence; let our hearts and minds be stirred.
send us forth to love and serve you, bring-ing peace where there is strife.
where tri-um-phant Love will wel-come those who had been last and least.

Nour-ish us with sa-cred sto-ry till we claim it as our own;
Give us, Christ, your great com-pas-sion to for-give as you for-gave;
There no more will en-vy blind us nor will pride our peace de-stroy,

teach us through this ho-ly ban-quet how to make Love's vic-to-ry known.
may we still be-hold your im-age in the world you died to save.
as we join with saints and an-gels to re-peat the sound-ing joy.

Text: Carl P. Daw, Jr. (b. 1944)
Music: J. Leavitt's *Christian Lyre*; harm. Ralph Vaughn Williams (1872-1958)
Text © 1989, Hope Publishing Co.; harm. © Oxford University Press, Inc.

87 87 D
PLEADING SAVIOR

As Your Family, Lord

1 As your fam - ily, Lord, meet us here. As your
2 At your ta - ble, Lord, we are fed. At your
3 Fill our spir - its, Lord, with your love. Fill our
4 Make us faith - ful, Lord, to your will. Make us
5 As your fam - ily, Lord, send us forth. As your

fam - ily, Lord, meet us here. As your fam - ily, Lord,
ta - ble, Lord, we are fed. At your ta - ble, Lord,
spir - its, Lord, with your love. Fill our spir - its, Lord,
faith - ful, Lord, to your will. Make us faith - ful, Lord,
fam - ily, Lord, send us forth. As your fam - ily, Lord,

meet us here. O Lord, speak your word.
we are fed. O Lord, feed us here.
with your love, O Lord, with your love.
to your will, O Lord, to your will.
send us forth. O Lord, send us forth.

Text: Anonymous
Music: African-American spiritual

888 5
KUM BA JAH

247 Table of Plenty

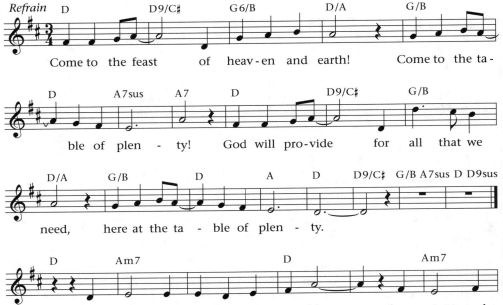

Refrain

Come to the feast of heav-en and earth! Come to the ta-
ble of plen - ty! God will pro-vide for all that we
need, here at the ta - ble of plen - ty.

1 O come and sit at my ta - ble where saints and
2 O come and eat with-out mon-ey; come to
3 My bread will ev - er sus - tain you through days of
4 Your fields will flow-er in full-ness; your homes will

sin - ners are friends. I wait to wel-come the lost and
drink with-out price. My feast of glad-ness will feed your
sor - row and woe. My wine will flow like a sea of
flour - ish in peace. For I, the giv - er of home and

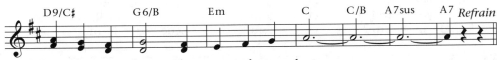

lone - ly to share the cup of my love. *Refrain*
spir - it with faith and full-ness of life.
glad-ness to flood the depths of your soul.
har - vest, will send my rain on the soil.

Text and music: Daniel L. Schutte (b. 1947)
© 1992, Daniel L. Schutte, admin. New Dawn Music/OCP Publications

Now the Feast and Celebration

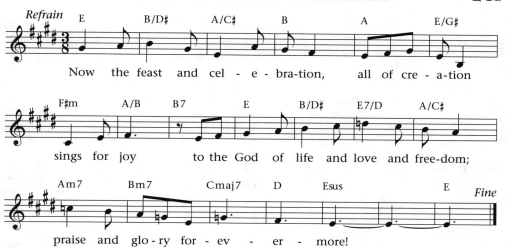

1 Now is the feast of the Lamb once slain,
whose blood has freed and united us
to be one great people of God. *Refrain*

2 Power and riches, wisdom and might,
all honor and glory to Christ forever. *Refrain*

3 For God has come to dwell with us,
to make us people of God,
to make all things new. *Refrain*

Text and music: Marty Haugen (b. 1950)
© 1990, GIA Publications, Inc.

249 Remembering with Love and Hope

1 Re - mem - ber - ing with love and hope, we
2 God's Word made known in flesh and blood, a
3 Through all our lives, Lord, you are near, and
4 We break the bread and bless the cup; your
5 We trust this pledge of your strong love and

cel - e - brate the feast. Christ bids us come and
cov - e - nant of grace; in man - ger, cross, and
to the end of time. In bread and cup your -
Spir - it is out-poured. Made one in you, we
pray, your king - dom come, when face to face we'll

dine with him, our Host and great High Priest.
emp - ty tomb, we see God's lov - ing face.
self you give; our life in yours we find.
feast in love un - til you come, O Lord.
feast with you in our e - ter - nal home.

Text: John Paarlberg (b. 1950)
Tune: American; harm. Annabel Morris Buchanan (1889-1983)

Text © 2000, John Paarlberg

CM
LAND OF REST

Great Prayer of Thanksgiving   250

The Lord be with you.
And also with you.
Lift up your hearts!
We lift them to the Lord.
Let us give thanks to the Lord our God.
It is right to give our thanks and praise.

Holy and right it is, and our joyful duty to give thanks to you at all times and in all places, O Lord our Creator, almighty and everlasting God! You created heaven with all its hosts and the earth with all its plenty. You have given us life and being, and preserve us by your providence. But you have shown us the fullness of your love in sending into the world your Son, Jesus Christ, the eternal Word, made flesh for us and for our salvation. For the precious gift of this mighty Savior who has reconciled us to you we praise and bless you, O God. With your whole Church on earth and with all the company of heaven we worship and adore your glorious name:

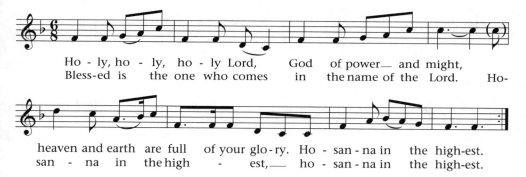

Ho - ly, ho - ly, ho - ly Lord, God of power— and might,
Bless-ed is the one who comes in the name of the Lord. Ho-

heaven and earth are full of your glo-ry. Ho - san - na in the high-est.
san - na in the high - est,— ho - san - na in the high-est.

Most righteous God, we remember in this Supper the perfect sacrifice offered once on the cross by our Lord Jesus Christ for the sin of the whole world. In the joy of his resurrection and in expectation of his coming again, we offer ourselves to you as holy and living sacrifices. Together we proclaim the mystery of the faith:

Christ has died. Christ is ris-en. Christ will come a - gain.

Send your Holy Spirit upon us, we pray, that the bread which we break and the cup which we bless may be to us the communion of the body and blood of Christ. Grant that, being joined together in him, we may attain to the unity of the faith and grow up in all things into Christ our Lord.

And as this grain has been gathered from many fields into one loaf, and these grapes from many hills into one cup, grant, O Lord, that your whole Church may soon be gathered from the ends of the earth into your kingdom. Even so, come, Lord Jesus!

251   Holy, Holy, Holy Is the Lord of Hosts

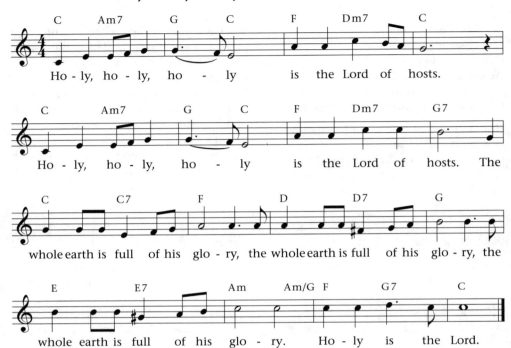

Ho - ly, ho - ly, ho - ly is the Lord of hosts.

Ho - ly, ho - ly, ho - ly is the Lord of hosts. The

whole earth is full of his glo - ry, the whole earth is full of his glo - ry, the

whole earth is full of his glo - ry. Ho - ly is the Lord.

Text and music: Nolene Prince (20th cent.), based on Isaiah 6:3

Holy, Holy, Holy Lord

Text: *Sanctus* (Isaiah 6:3; Psalm 118:26)
Music: Grayson Warren Brown (b. 1948); arr. Larry Adams

Music © 1979, Grayson Warren Brown, admin. OCP Publications

253 Lamb of God

Text: *Agnus Dei* (John 1:29)
Music: The Iona Community

Eat This Bread

1 Christ is the bread of life,
   the true bread sent from the Father. *Refrain*

2 Our ancestors ate manna in the desert,
   but this is the bread come down from heaven. *Refrain*

3 Eat his flesh and drink his blood,
   and Christ will raise you up on the last day. *Refrain*

4 Anyone who eats this bread
   will live forever. *Refrain*

5 If you believe and eat this bread,
   you will have eternal life. *Refrain*

Text: From John 6; para. Robert Batastini (b. 1942) and The Community of Taizé
Music: Jacques Berthier (1923-1994)

EAT THIS BREAD

255

Psalm 34

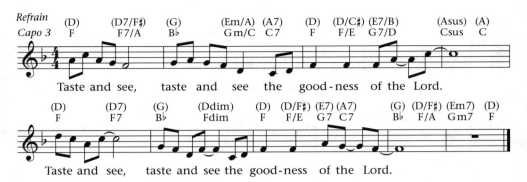

Taste and see, taste and see the good-ness of the Lord.

Taste and see, taste and see the good-ness of the Lord.

Refrain

¹ I will bless the LORD at all times;
    his praise shall continually be in my
    mouth.
² **My soul makes its boast in the LORD;**
    let the humble hear and be glad.
³ O magnify the LORD with me,
    and let us exalt his name together.

Refrain

⁴ I sought the LORD, and he answered me,
    and delivered me from all my fears.
⁵ **Look to him, and be radiant;**
    so your faces shall never be ashamed.
⁶ This poor soul cried, and was heard by
    the LORD,
    and was saved from every trouble.
⁷ **The angel of the LORD encamps**
    around those who fear him, and
    delivers them.

Refrain

⁸ O taste and see that the LORD is good;
    happy are those who take refuge in
    him.
⁹ **O fear the LORD, you his holy ones,**
    for those who fear him have no want.
¹⁰ The young lions suffer want and hunger,
    but those who seek the LORD lack no
    good thing.

Refrain

¹¹ Come, O children, listen to me;
    I will teach you the fear of the LORD.
¹² Which of you desires life,
    and covets many days to enjoy good?
¹³ **Keep your tongue from evil,**
    and your lips from speaking deceit.
¹⁴ **Depart from evil, and do good;**
    seek peace, and pursue it.

Refrain

Refrain text: Psalm 34:8
Music: Francis Patrick O'Brien

Psalm 103: Bless the Lord, My Soul

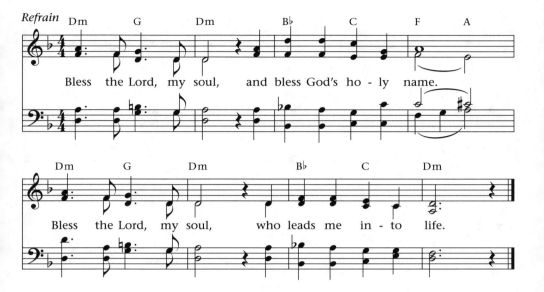

1 It is God who forgives all your guilt,
who heals every one of your ills,
who redeems your life from the grave,
who crowns you with love and compassion. *Refrain*

2 The Lord is compassion and love,
slow to anger and rich in mercy.
God does not treat us according to our sins
nor repay us according to our faults. *Refrain*

3 As a father has compassion on his children,
the Lord has pity on those who fear him,
for God knows of what we are made,
God remembers that we are dust. *Refrain*

Text: from Psalm 103; para. Robert Batastini (b. 1942) and The Community of Taizé
Music: Jacques Berthier (1923-1994)

257 This Is the Threefold Truth

1 This is the three-fold truth on which our faith de-pends,
2 Made sa-cred by long use, new - mint-ed for our time,
3 On this we fix our minds as, kneel-ing side by side,
4 By this we are up-held when doubt or grief as - sails
5 This is the three-fold truth which, if we hold it fast,

and with this joy - ful cry____ wor - ship be-gins and ends:
our lit - ur - gies sum up the hope we__ have in him:
we take the bread and wine from him, the__ cru - ci - fied:
our Chris-tian for - ti - tude, and on - ly__ grace a - vails:
chang - es the world and us and brings us__ home at last:

Christ has died! Christ is ris - en! Christ will come a - gain!

Text: Fred Pratt Green (1903-2000)
Music: Jack Schrader (b. 1942)

© 1980, Hope Publishing Co.

12 12 12
ACCLAMATIONS

Let Us Talents and Tongues Employ

258

1 Let us tal - ents and tongues em - ploy, reach - ing out with a
2 Christ is a - ble to make us one. At the ta - ble he
3 Je - sus calls us in, sends us out bear - ing fruit in a

shout of joy. Bread is bro - ken, the wine is poured,
sets the tone, teach - ing peo - ple to live to bless,
world of doubt, gives us love to tell, bread to share.

Refrain

Christ is spo - ken and seen and heard.
love in word and in deed ex - press. Je - sus lives a - gain,
God (Im - man - u - el) ev - ery - where!

earth can breathe a - gain, pass the Word a - round: loaves a - bound!

Text: Fred Kaan (b. 1929)
Music: Jamaican folk tune; adapt. Doreen Potter (1925-1980)
Text and adapt. © 1975, Hope Publishing Co.

LM with refrain
LINSTEAD

259 Santo, santo, santo / Holy, Holy, Holy

Capo 3

Spanish: San-to, san-to, san-to, san-to, san-to, san-to es nues-tro Dios,
English: Ho-ly, ho-ly, ho-ly, ho-ly, ho-ly, ho-ly is our God,

Se-ñor de to-da la tie-rra, san-to, san-to es nues-tro Dios.
God the Lord of earth and heav-en; ho-ly, ho-ly is our God.

San-to, san-to, san-to, san-to, san-to, san-to es nues-tro Dios,
Ho-ly, ho-ly, ho-ly, ho-ly, ho-ly, ho-ly is our God,

Se-ñor de to-da la his-to-ria, san-to, san-to es nues-tro Dios.
God the Lord of all of his-tory, ho-ly, ho-ly is our God.

Que a-com-pa-ña a nues-tro pue-blo, que vi-ve en nues-tras
Who ac-com-pan-ies our peo-ple, who lives with-in our

lu-chas, del u-ni-ver-so en-te-ro el
strug-gles, of all the earth and heav-en the

ú-ni-co Se-ñor. Ben-di-tos los que en su
one and on-ly Lord. Bless-ed those who in the

Text and music: Guillermo Cuéllar (b. 1955), from *La Misa Popular Salvadoreña;*
tr. Linda McCrae (b. 20th cent.)

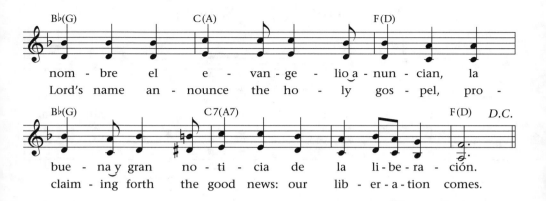

nom - bre el e - van - ge - lio a - nun - cian, la
Lord's name an - nounce the ho - ly gos - pel, pro -

bue - na y gran no - ti - cia de la li - be - ra - ción.
claim - ing forth the good news: our lib - er - a - tion comes.

Somos pueblo que camina / We Are People on a Journey

260

Spanish 1 So - mos pue - blo que ca - mi - na por la sen - da del do - lor.
2 Los hu - mil - des y los po - bres in - vi - ta - dos son de Dios.

English 1 We are peo - ple on a jour - ney; pain is with us all the way.
2 God has sent the in - vi - ta - tion to the hum - ble and the poor.

Estribillo (Refrain)

A - cu - da - mos ju - bi - lo - sos a la san - ta co - mu - nión.
Joy - ful - ly we come to - geth - er at the ho - ly feast of God.

3 Este pan que Dios nos brinda
alimenta nuestra unión. *Estribillo*

3 This is bread that God provides us,
nourishing our unity. *Refrain*

4 Cristo aquí se hace presente;
al reunirnos en su amor. *Estribillo*

4 Christ is ever present with us
to unite us all in love. *Refrain*

5 Los sedientos de justicia
buscan su liberación. *Estribillo*

5 All who truly thirst for justice
seek their liberation here. *Refrain*

Text and music: La Misa Popular Nicaragüense (20th cent.); tr. Carolyn Jennings (b. 1936)

SOMOS PUEBLOS

Tr. © 1993, The Pilgrim Press

261

Haleluya! Pelo tsa rona /
Hallelujah! We Sing Your Praises

Shona Ha - le - lu - ya! Pe - lo tsa ro - na, di tha -
English Hal - le - lu - jah! We sing your prais - es, all our

bi - le ka - o - fe - la. Ha - le - lu - ya! Pe - lo tsa
hearts are filled with glad - ness. Hal - le - lu - jah! We sing your

ro - na, di tha - bi - le ka - o - fe - la.
prais - es, all our hearts are filled with glad - ness.

1 Christ the Lord to us said: I am wine, I am bread, I am
2 Now he sends us all out, strong in faith, a-mid doubt, strong in

Text and music: South African

© 1984 Utryck, admin. Walton Music Corp.

HALELUYA! PELO TSO RONA

This Is the Feast of Victory 262

Refrain
This is the feast of vic-to-ry for our God. Hal-le-
lu - jah, hal-le-lu-jah, hal-le - lu - jah! lu - jah!

To stanzas   Last time

1 Wor-thy is Christ, the Lamb who was slain, whose
2 Pow - er, rich - es, wis - dom and strength and
3 Sing with all the peo - ple of God, and
4 Bless - ing, hon - or, glo - ry and might be to
5 For the Lamb who was slain has be -

blood set us free to be peo - ple of God.
hon - or, bless - ing and glo - ry are his.
join in the hymn of all cre - a - tion.
God and the Lamb for - ev - er. A - men.
gun his reign. Hal - le - lu - jah!

Text: Revelation 6:12-14; para. John W. Arthur (1922-1980)
Music: Richard Hillert (b. 1923)

9 11 with refrain
FESTIVAL CANTICLE

263   Open Our Eyes

Text and music: Kevin Keil

© 1998, Lorenz Publishing Co.

Gm/D(F#m/C#) Cm(Bm)   Gm/B♭ (F#m/A)   A♭(G)   Gm(F#m)

1 To   the   ones   bro-ken - heart - ed:
2 To   the   vic - tims of   vio - lence:
3 When a   col - or di - vides us: O - pen our eyes.
4 To those full   of life's   sor - row:
5 To those suf - fer - ing   ill - ness:

Fm(Em)   Gm(F#m)   A♭(G)   B♭(A)

To   the   plight   of the   poor:
To   the   ones   who seek   jus - tice:
When the   dark - ness sur - rounds us: O - pen our eyes.
To   the   needs   of the   low - ly:
To those trapped   by ad - dic - tion:

A♭(G)   E♭/G(D/F#)   G♭2(F2)   C♭maj9 (B♭maj9)

To   the   in - no-cent chil-dren:
To those sit - ting in pris - on:
When we choose to look else-where: O - pen our eyes.
To   the   ones who seek peace:___
To those lost   or for - got - ten:

D♭(C)   A♭m/C♭ (Gm/B♭)   A♭/B♭(G/A)   B♭(A)   *Refrain*

Teach   us   com - pas - sion   and   love.

Coda

A♭maj7(Gmaj7)   D♭(C)   B♭m7(Am7) E♭2(D2)   E♭(D)

O - pen   our   eyes   once a - gain.

264 When a Prophet Sings of Justice

1 When a proph - et sings of jus - tice like broad riv - ers
2 When a gos - pel speaks of hun - ger for the Word and
3 When an old song can re - mind us of how sim - ple
4 As you grant us bet - ter in - sight with the vi - sion

flow - ing free, let me clear - ly see the vi - sion
for the bread, let me hear how with each feed - ing
gifts can be, God, you let us come to - geth - er,
your grace gives, help us make the wis - er choic - es,

of an earth that might yet be: God's in - ten - tion, hu - man dreams,
of the hun - gry, Christ is fed: how, as we at - tend their cry,
from our self - ish selves set free, freed from pomp and cir - cum - stance,
sim - plest of al - ter - na - tives; stripped of emp - ty act and talk

righ - teous - ness like might - y streams, wa - ters
loaves and fish - es mul - ti - ply in a
free to join in Christ's own dance, turned 'round
we may take a hum - bler walk, jus - tice,

Text: John Core (b. 1951)
Music: Louis Bourgeois (c. 1510-c. 1561); arr. Johann Crüger (1598-1662)
Text © 1998, Selah Publishing Co., Inc.

87 87 77 88
GENEVAN 42

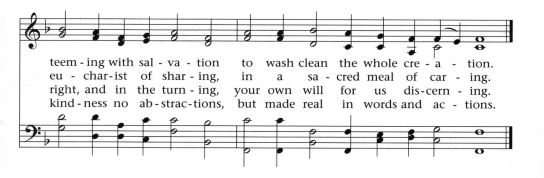

teem - ing with sal - va - tion to wash clean the whole cre - a - tion.
eu - char-ist of shar - ing, in a sa - cred meal of car - ing.
right, and in the turn - ing, your own will for us dis-cern - ing.
kind - ness no ab-strac-tions, but made real in words and ac - tions.

When the Church of Jesus 265

1 When the church of Je - sus shuts its out - er door,
2 If our hearts are lift - ed where de - vo - tion soars
3 Lest the gifts we of - fer— mon - ey, tal - ents, time—

lest the roar of traf - fic drown the voice of prayer,
high a - bove this hun - gry, suf - fering world of ours,
serve to salve our con - science, to our se - cret shame,

may our prayers, Lord, make us ten times more a - ware
lest our hymns should drug us to for - get its needs,
Lord, re - prove, in - spire us by the way you give;

that the world we ban - ish is our Chris - tian care.
forge our Chris-tian wor - ship in - to Chris - tian deeds.
teach us, ris - en Sav - ior, how true Chris - tians live.

Text: Fred Pratt Green (1903-2000), based on James 2:14-17
Music: Ralph Vaughan Williams (1872-1958)

65 65 D
KING'S WESTON

266 Our Cities Cry to You, O God

1 Our cit - ies cry to you, O God, from out their pain and strife;
2 Yet still you walk our streets, O Christ! We know your pres - ence here
3 Your peo - ple are your hands and feet to serve your world to - day;
4 O heal - ing Sav - ior, Prince of Peace, sal - va - tion's source and sum,

you made us for your - self a - lone, but we choose al - ien life.
where hum - ble Chris - tians love and serve in god - ly grace and fear.
our lives the book our cit - ies read to help them find your way.
for you our bro - ken cit - ies cry: O come, Lord Je - sus, come!

Our goals are plea - sure, gold, and power; in - jus - tice stalks our earth;
O Word made flesh, be seen in us! May all we say and do
O pour your sov - ereign Spir - it out on heart and will and brain:
With truth your roy - al di - a - dem, with right-teous-ness your rod,

in vain we seek for rest, for joy, for sense of hu - man worth.
af - firm you God In - car - nate still and turn sad hearts to you!
in - spire your Church with love and power to ease our cit - ies' pain!
O come, Lord Je - sus, bring to earth the cit - y of our God!

Text: Margaret Clarkson (b. 1915)
Music: *Kentucky Harmony* (1816)
Text © 1987, Hope Publishing Co.

CMD
SALVATION

Will You Come and Follow Me

1 Will you come and fol-low me if I but call your name?
2 Will you leave your-self be-hind if I but call your name?
3 Will you let the blind-ed see if I but call your name?
4 Will you love the 'you' you hide if I but call your name?
5 Lord, your sum-mons ech-oes true when you but call my name.

Will you go where you don't know and nev-er be the same?
Will you care for cruel and kind and nev-er be the same?
Will you set the pris-oners free and nev-er be the same?
Will you quell the fear in-side and nev-er be the same?
Let me turn and fol-low you and nev-er be the same.

Will you let my love be shown, will you let my name be known,
Will you risk the hos-tile stare should your life at-tract or scare?
Will you kiss the lep-er clean, and do such as this un-seen,
Will you use the faith you've found to re-shape the world a-round,
In your com-pa-ny I'll go where your love and foot-steps show.

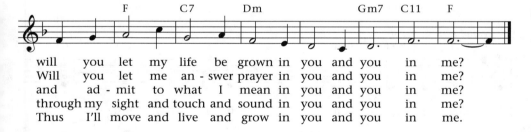

will you let my life be grown in you and you in me?
Will you let me an-swer prayer in you and you in me?
and ad-mit to what I mean in you and you in me?
through my sight and touch and sound in you and you in me?
Thus I'll move and live and grow in you and you in me.

Text: The Iona Community
Music: Scottish traditional

76 76 77 76
KELVINGROVE

268 Here I Am, Lord

1 I, the Lord of sea and sky,
I who made the stars of night,
2 I, the Lord of snow and rain,
I will break their hearts of stone,
3 I, the Lord of wind and flame,
Fin-est bread I will pro - vide

I have heard my
I will make their
I have borne my
give them hearts for
I will tend the
till their hearts be

peo - ple cry.
dark - ness bright.
peo - ple's pain.
love a - lone.
poor and lame.
sat - is - fied.

All who dwell in dark and sin
Who will bear my light to them?
I have wept for love of them.
I will speak my word to them.
I will set a feast for them.
I will give my life to them.

my hand will save.
They turn a - way.
My hand will save.

Whom shall I send?
Whom shall I send?
Whom shall I send?

Refrain

Here I am, Lord. Is it I, Lord?

Text and music: Daniel L. Schutte (b. 1947); arr. Michael Pope and John Weissrock
© 1981, Daniel L. Schutte, admin. New Dawn Music/OCP Publications

77 74 D with refrain
HERE I AM, LORD

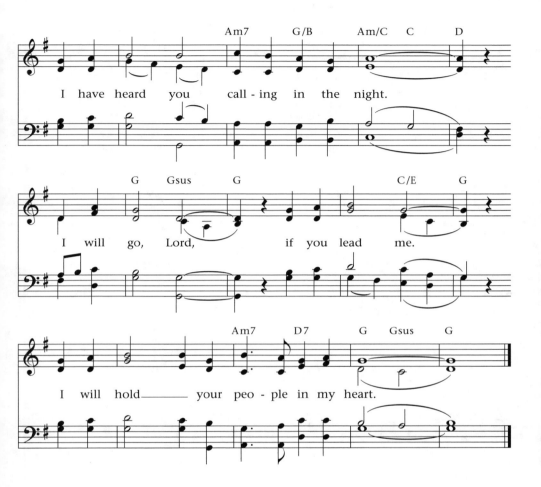

269

Tú has venido a la orilla /
You Have Come Down to the Lakeshore

Spanish 1 Tú has ve - ni - do a la o - ri - lla,
2 Tú sa - bes bien lo que ten - go;

English 1 You have come down to the lake - shore,
2 You know full well what I have, Lord:

no has bus - ca - do ni a sa - bios ni a ri - cos;
en mi bar - ca no hay o - ro ni es - pa - das,
seek - ing nei - ther the wise nor the wealth - y,
nei - ther trea - sure nor wea - pons for con - quest,

tan só - lo quie - ras que yo te si - ga.
tan só - lo re - des y mi tra - ba - jo.
but on - ly ask - ing for me to fol - low.
just these my fish - nets and will for work - ing.

Estribillo/Refrain

Se - ñor, me has mi - ra - do a los o - jos,
O Lord, you have looked in - to my eyes;

son - ri - en - do has di - cho mi nom - bre,
kind - ly smil - ing, you've called out my name.

en la a - re - na he de - ja - do mi bar - ca,
On the sand I have a - ban - doned my small boat;

Text and music: Cesáreo Gabaraín (1936-1991); tr. Madeleine Forell Marshall (b. 1946)

© 1979, Cesáreo Gabaraín, admin. OCP Publications

8 10 10 with refrain

PESCADOR DE HOMBRES

junto a ti   buscaré otro mar.
now with you,   I will seek oth - er seas.

3 Tú necesitas mis manos,
  mi cansancio que a otros descanse,
  amor que quiera seguir amando.

4 Tú, pescador de otros lagos,
  ansia eterna de almas que esperan,
  amigo bueno, que así me llamas.

3 You need my hands, my exhaustion,
  working love for the rest of the weary,
  a love that's willing to go on loving.

4 You who have fished other waters,
  you, the longing of souls that are yearning:
  O loving Friend, you have come to call me.

In Labor All Creation Groans   270

1 In la - bor all cre - a - tion groans till fear and ha - tred cease,
2 In la - bor all cre - a - tion groans till un - just wa - ges cease,
3 In la - bor all cre - a - tion groans till prej - u - dice shall cease,
4 In la - bor all cre - a - tion groans till vio - lent crime shall cease,
5 In la - bor all cre - a - tion groans till rape and mur - der cease,

till hu - man hearts have un - der - stood: in Christ a - lone is peace.
till poor are clothed and chil - dren fed and Christ be - comes their peace.
till ev - ery gen - der, race, and creed in Christ will live in peace.
till force gives way to gen - tle - ness and Christ be - comes our peace.
till wom - en walk by night un - harmed and Christ is this world's peace.

6 In labor all creation groans
  till false divisions cease,
  till diff'rences are reconciled
  in Christ who is our peace.

7 In labor all creation groans,
  God's justice to increase.
  When right in place of might prevails,
  then Christ will be our peace.

Text: Delores Dufner (b. 1939)
Music: Supplement to *Kentucky Harmony* (1820)
Text © 1992, 1993, The Sisters of St. Benedict, admin. OCP Publications

CM
DETROIT

271 What God Requires

With what shall we come before the LORD, and bow ourselves before God on high?

He has told you, O mortal, what is good.
And what does the Lord require of you?

To do justice, to love kindness, and to walk humbly with our God.

—Micah 6:6, 8

272 O God, Your Justice Towers

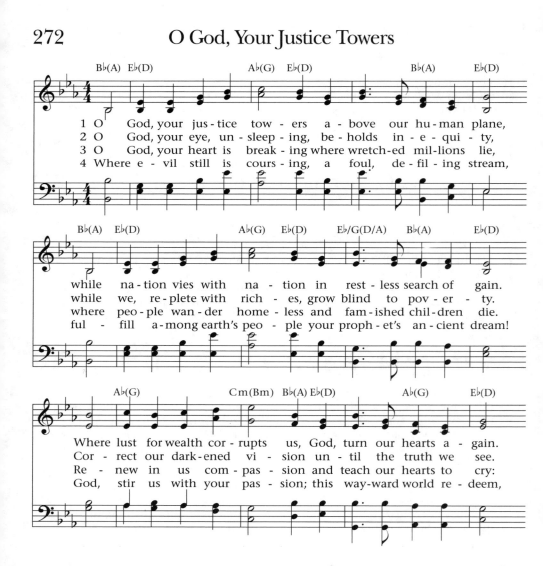

1 O God, your jus-tice tow - ers a - bove our hu-man plane,
2 O God, your eye, un - sleep-ing, be - holds in - e - qui - ty,
3 O God, your heart is break - ing where wretch-ed mil-lions lie,
4 Where e - vil still is cours-ing, a foul, de - fil - ing stream,

while na - tion vies with na - tion in rest - less search of gain.
while we, re - plete with rich - es, grow blind to pov - er - ty.
where peo - ple wan - der home - less and fam - ished chil - dren die.
ful - fill a - mong earth's peo - ple your proph - et's an - cient dream!

Where lust for wealth cor - rupts us, God, turn our hearts a - gain.
Cor - rect our dark - ened vi - sion un - til the truth we see.
Re - new in us com - pas - sion and teach our hearts to cry:
God, stir us with your pas - sion; this way-ward world re - deem,

Text: Herman G. Stuempfle, Jr.(b. 1923)
Music: W. Walker's *Southern Harmony* (1835); harm. Emily R. Brink (b. 1940)
Text © 1998, Selah Publishing Co., Inc.; harm. © 2001, CRC Publications

76 76 D
COMPLAINER

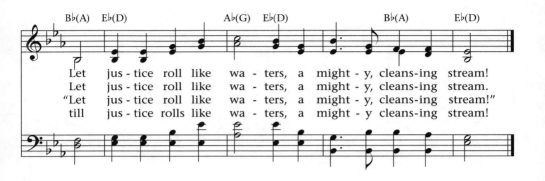

Let jus-tice roll like wa-ters, a might-y, cleans-ing stream!
Let jus-tice roll like wa-ters, a might-y, cleans-ing stream.
"Let jus-tice roll like wa-ters, a might-y, cleans-ing stream!"
till jus-tice rolls like wa-ters, a might-y cleans-ing stream!

Psalm 112

273

Hap-py are they who de-light, who de-light in the law of God.

Refrain

[1] Praise the LORD!
Happy are those who fear the LORD,
who greatly delight in his
commandments.

[2] **Their descendants will be mighty in the
land;
the generation of the upright will be
blessed.**

[3] Wealth and riches are in their houses,
and their righteousness endures
forever.

[4] **They rise in the darkness as a light for the
upright;
they are gracious, merciful, and
righteous.**

[5] It is well with those who deal generously
and lend,
who conduct their affairs with justice.

Refrain

[6] For the righteous will never be moved;
they will be remembered forever.

[7] **They are not afraid of evil tidings;
their hearts are firm, secure in the
LORD.**

[8] Their hearts are steady, they will not be
afraid;
in the end they will look in triumph on
their foes.

[9] **They have distributed freely, they have
given to the poor;
their righteousness endures forever;
their horn is exalted in honor.**

[10] The wicked see it and are angry;
they gnash their teeth and melt away;
the desire of the wicked comes to
nothing.

Refrain

274 If You and I Believe in Christ

1 If you and I be-lieve in Christ and we to-geth-er pray,
2 If you and I re-main in Christ and we to-geth-er pray,
3 If you and I have faith in Christ and we to-geth-er pray,

the Ho-ly Spir-it will come down and set God's peo-ple free,
the Ho-ly Bi-ble teach-es us that God will hear our prayer,
the Ho-ly Spir-it shows us how to fol-low in God's way,

and set God's peo-ple free, and set God's peo-ple free;
that God will hear our prayer, that God will hear our prayer;
to fol-low in God's way, to fol-low in God's way;

the Ho-ly Spir-it will come down and set God's peo-ple free.
the Ho-ly Bi-ble teach-es us that God will hear our prayer.
the Ho-ly Spir-it will lead us to fol-low in God's way.

Text: St. 1 from Zimbabwe; st. 2-3, Bert Polman (b. 1945)
Music: from Zimbabwe, as adapted from an English song

Text, st. 2-3, © 2001, CRC Publications

Not for Tongues of Heaven's Angels

1 Not for tongues of heav-en's an - gels, not for
2 Love is hum - ble; love is gen - tle; love is
3 Nev - er jeal - ous, nev - er self - ish, love will
4 In the day this world is fad - ing faith and

wis - dom to dis - cern, not for faith that mas-ters
ten - der, true, and kind; love is gra - cious, ev - er
not re - joice in wrong; nev - er boast - ful nor re -
hope will play their part; but when Christ is seen in

moun - tains, for this bet - ter gift we yearn:
pa - tient, gen - er - ous of heart and mind:
sent - ful, love be - lieves and suf - fers long:
glo - ry, love shall reign in ev - ery heart:

may love be ours, O Lord.

Text: Timothy Dudley-Smith (b. 1926), based on 1 Corinthians 13
Music: Roy Hopp (b. 1951)

87 87 6
REINLYN

Text © 1985, Hope Publishing Co.; music © 1990, Selah Publishing Co., Inc.

276   Psalm 133

Refrain

How ver-y good and pleas-ant when we live in u-ni-ty.
It is like pre-cious oil, like fresh morn-ing
dew. We gath-er here to-geth-er with our hearts and voic-es
raised to God, who's the cen-ter of our u-ni-ty in praise!

Refrain

¹ How very good and pleasant it is
    when kindred live together in unity!
² It is like the precious oil on the head,
    running down upon the beard,
on the beard of Aaron,
    running down over the collar of his robes.
³ It is like the dew of Hermon,
    which falls on the mountains of Zion.
For there the Lord ordained his blessing,
    life forevermore.

Refrain

The Servant Song

1 Will you let me be your ser-vant, let me be as
2 We are pil-grims on a jour-ney; we are trav-'lers
3 I will hold the Christ-light for you in the night-time
4 I will weep when you are weep-ing; when you laugh, I'll
5 Will you let me be your ser-vant, let me be as

Christ to you? Pray that I may have the grace to
on the road. We are here to help each oth-er
of your fear. I will hold my hand out to you,
laugh with you. I will share your joy and sor-row
Christ to you? Pray that I may have the grace to

let you be my ser - vant too.
walk the mile and bear the load.
speak the peace you long to hear.
till we've seen this jour - ney through.
let you be my ser - vant too.

Text and music: Richard Gillard (b. 1953); harm. Betty Pulkingham (b. 1929)

Go into All the World

Go in-to all the world pro-claim-ing the Good News!

Tell ev'-ry-one that Je-sus died to set them free.
free, to set them

Tell of his love un-til he comes in glo-ry
free.

to make our home with him e-ter-nal-ly!

Text and music: Barbara Boertje (b. 1959), based on Matthew 28:19-20
© 1995, Barbara Boertje

Through All the World

1 Through all the world let ev-ery na-tion sing to God, the king!
2 Through all the world let ev-ery one ex-press true righ-teous-ness!
3 Through all the world let ev-ery one em-brace the gift of grace!
4 If all the world in ev-ery part shall hear and God re-vere,

As Lord may Christ pre-side where now he is de-fied,
May Christ be now the norm to which we all con-form,
May Christ's great light con-sume our cit-ies' dark-est gloom,
we must be moved to care and in his name to share

and sov-ereign place his throne in lands not yet his own.
his pas-sion cure the sin that fes-ters from with-in.
may Christ's great love ef-face hos-til-i-ties of race.
the lib-er-at-ing Word which must be told a-broad.

Through all the world let ev-ery na-tion sing to God, the King!
Through all the world let ev-ery one ex-press true righ-teous-ness!
Through all the world let ev-ery one em-brace the gift of grace!
Then all the world in ev-ery part shall hear and God re-vere!

Text: Bryan Jeffery Leech (b. 1931)
Music: Paul F. Liljestrand (b. 1931)
© 1970, The Hymn Society, admin. Hope Publishing Co.

10 4 66 66 10 4
CONRAD

280 Thuma mina / Send Me, Lord

Text and music: South African
© 1984, Utryck, admin. Walton Music Corp.

THUMA MINA

Psalm 67

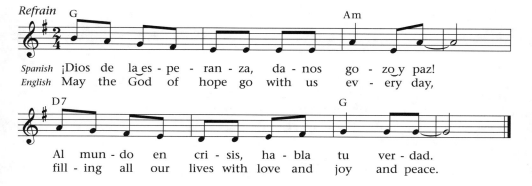

Spanish ¡Dios de la esperanza, danos gozo y paz!
English May the God of hope go with us every day,

Al mundo en crisis, habla tu verdad.
filling all our lives with love and joy and peace.

Refrain

¹ May God be gracious to us and bless us
   and make his face to shine upon us,
² that your way may be known upon earth,
   your saving power among all nations.

Refrain

³ Let the peoples praise you, O God;
   let all the peoples praise you.
⁴ Let the nations be glad and sing for joy,
   for you judge the peoples with equity
   and guide the nations upon earth.
⁵ Let the peoples praise you, O God;
   let all the peoples praise you.

Refrain

⁶ The earth has yielded its increase;
   God, our God, has blessed us.
⁷ May God continue to bless us;
   let all the ends of the earth revere him.

Refrain

Refrain: Argentine traditional; tr. Alvin Schutmaat (1921-1988)

ARGENTINA

282 Canto de esperanza / Song of Hope

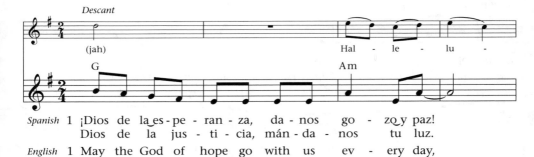

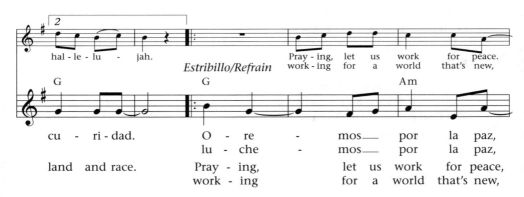

Text: St. 1 Spanish traditional, tr. Alvin Schutmaat (1921-1988); st. 2 Tom Mitchell (b. 1947),
Sp. tr. Frank W. Roman (b. 20th c.)
Music: Argentine folk melody
St. 2 © 1993, Choristers Guild

11 11 11 11 with refrain
ARGENTINA

Sing - ing, share our joy with all,
faith - ful when we hear Christ's call.

D 7   G

can - te   -   mos___ de   tu a - mor,
fie - les   a___ ti,   Se - ñor.

sing - ing,   share our   joy   with all,
faith - ful   when we   hear   Christ's call.

2 Dios será nuestro pastor en el camino
 no nos abandonará cuando nos perdimos.
 La vida es una carga pesada,
 Pero Dios siempre nos ayudará.   *Estribillo*

2 God will be our Shepherd as we go our way
 and will not forsake us when we go astray.
 Even though the load of life is hard to bear,
 we must not forget that God is always there.   *Refrain*

The Mission of God's People   283

Following the apostles, the church is sent—
sent with the gospel of the kingdom
to make disciples of all nations,
to feed the hungry,
and to proclaim the assurance
that in the name of Christ
there is forgiveness of sin and new life
for all who repent and believe.

The church is sent to tell the good news
that our world belongs to God.
In a world estranged from God,
where millions face confusing choices,
this mission is central to our being,
for we announce the one name that saves.

We repent of leaving this work to a few,
we pray for brothers and sisters
who suffer for the faith,
and rejoice that the Spirit
is waking us to see
our mission in God's world.

—*Our World Belongs to God*, st. 44

284   Go, My Children, with My Blessing

4 I, the Lord, will bless and keep you, and give you peace.

Capo 3

| (D) F | (G) B♭ | (Em) Gm | (A) C | (D) F | (G) B♭ | (A) C | (D) F |

1 Go, my chil-dren, with my bless-ing, nev - er a - lone.
2 Go, my chil-dren, sins for-giv-en, at peace and pure.
3 Go, my chil-dren, fed and nour-ished, clos - er to me.
4 I, the Lord, will bless and keep you, and give you peace.

I, the Lord, will smile up - on you, and give you peace.

| (D) F | (G) B♭ | (Em) Gm | (A) C | (G) B♭ | (A) C | (D) F |

Wak - ing, sleep-ing, I am with you, you are my own.
Here you learned how much I love you, what I can cure.
Grow in love and love by serv-ing, joy - ful and free.
I, the Lord, will smile up - on you, and give you peace.

Text: Jaroslav J. Vajda (b. 1919)
Music: Welsh melody (c. 1784); desc. Hal Hopson (b. 1933)

84 84 88 84
AR HYD Y NOS

I, the Lord, will be your Fa - ther, Sav - ior, Com - fort - er.

(G) (D) (G) (D) (G) (Am) (G) (D) (Em) (D) (Em)(Bm) (Em) (Asus) (A)
B♭ F B♭ F B♭ Cm B♭ F Gm F Gm Dm Gm Csus C

In my love's bap - tis - mal riv - er, I have made you mine for - ev - er.
Here you heard my dear Son's sto - ry, here you touched him, saw his glo - ry.
Here my Spir - it's pow - er filled you, here his ten - der com-fort stilled you.
I, the Lord, will be your Fa - ther, Sav - ior, Com-fort - er, and Broth-er.

Go, my chil - dren. I will keep you, and give you peace.

(D) (G) (Em) (A) (D) (G) (A) (D)
F B♭ Gm C F B♭ C F

Go, my chil - dren, with my bless - ing, you are my own.
Go, my chil - dren, sins for - giv - en, at peace and pure.
Go, my chil - dren, fed and nour-ished, joy - ful and free.
Go, my chil - dren. I will keep you, and give you peace.

285   May the Lord, Mighty God

Descant

2 Lift up and see God's face, full of

1 May the Lord, might-y God, bless and
2 Lift up your eyes and see God's face, full of

grace for-ev-er; May the Lord,

keep you for-ev-er; grant you peace,
grace for-ev-er; may the Lord,

might-y God, bless and keep you for-ev-er.

per-fect peace, cour-age in ev-ery en-deav-or.
might-y God, bless and keep you for-ev-er.

Text: based on Numbers 6:24-26
Music: Chinese folk tune; attr. to Pao-chen Li (1907-1979)

286   Amen!

Canon (1) (2) (3) (4)

A-men, a-men, al-le-lu-ia, a-men.

Music: John L. Bell (b. 1949)
© 1995, WGRG the Iona Community (Scotland), admin. GIA Publications, Inc.

Amen, siakudu misa / Amen, We Praise Your Name, O God

Text and music: S. C. Molefe (1921-1983), South African; tr. David Dargie (b. 1938)

MASITHI

© 1991, Lumko Institute

288

Benediction/
My Friends, May You Grow in Grace

My friends, may you grow in grace, and in the knowl-edge of our Lord and Sav - ior. My friends, may you grow in grace, and in the knowl-edge of Je - sus Christ. To God be the glo - ry, now and for - ev - er, now and for - ev - er, a - men. To God be the glo - ry, now and for - ev - er, now and for - ev - er, a - men.

Text and music: Timothy James Meaney (b. 1965) and Sean Diamond (b. 1968); rev. Gregg DeMey (b. 1972) and Gregory Kett (b. 1970)

Now Go in Peace

289

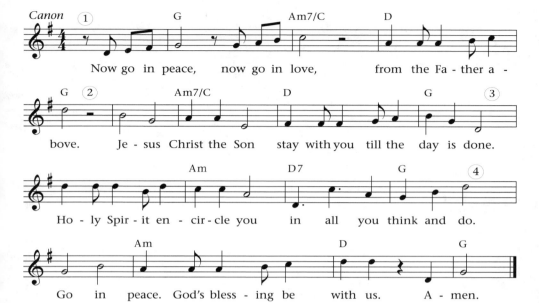

Now go in peace, now go in love, from the Fa - ther a -
bove. Je - sus Christ the Son stay with you till the day is done.
Ho - ly Spir - it en - cir - cle you in all you think and do.
Go in peace. God's bless - ing be with us. A - men.

Text: Michael Mair (b. 1942)
Music: Caribbean folk tune

JUNKANOO

Text © Church of Scotland Panel on Worship

Sixfold Amen

290

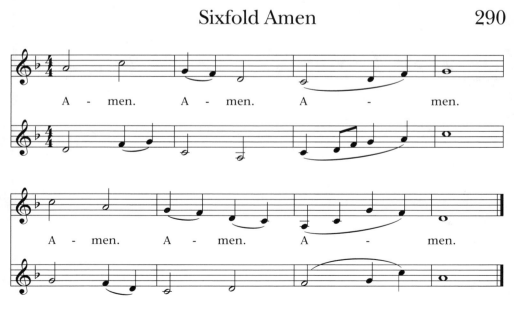

A - men. A - men. A - men.

A - men. A - men. A - men.

Music: Chinese folk melody; arr. Puqi Jiang

Arr. © Puqi Jiang

291 The Lord Bless You and Keep You

Text: Numbers 6:24-26
Music: Barbara Boertje (b. 1959)

Song of Simeon /
Lord, Bid Your Servant Go in Peace

292

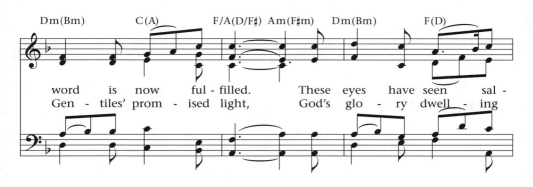

Text: Luke 2:29-32; para. James Quinn, S. J. (b. 1919)
Music: American folk melody; harm. Annabel Morris Buchanan (1889-1983)

CM
LAND OF REST

293

Siyahamba /
We Are Marching in the Light of God

Zulu: Si - ya - hamb' e - ku - kha - nyen' kwen - khos', si - ya -
English: We are march - ing* in the light of God, we are
Spanish: Ca - mi - nan - do en la luz de Dios, ca - mi -

nyen' kwen khos'.
light of God.
luz de Dios.

hamb' e - ku - kha - nyen' kwen - khos'. nyen' kwen kha -
march - ing in the light of God. light of, the
nan - do en la luz de Dios. luz de la

(khos') Si - ya - ham - ba
(God) We are march - ing
(Dios) Ca - mi - nan - do

nyen' kwen - khos'. Si - ya - ham - ba, ham - ba, si - ya -
light of God. We are march - ing, march - ing, we are
luz de Dios. Ca - mi - nan - do va - mos, ca - mi -

alternate text: dancing, praying, singing

Text and music: South African (20th cent.)
© 1984, Utryck, admin. Walton Music Corp.

SIYAHAMBA

nyen' kwen   khos'.
light   of   God.
luz   de   Dios.

G   Ooo   D7   ┌─3─┐   G

ham - ba,   ham - ba si - ya - hamb' e - ku - kha - nyen' kwen   kha -
march-ing,   march-ing, we are march-ing   in   the   light   of,   the
nan - do,   va - mos, ca - mi - nan - do en   la   luz   de,   la

┌─3─┘

(khos')   Si - ya - ham - ba_____
(God)   We   are march - ing_____
(Dios)   Ca - mi - nan - do_____

G7   C

nyen' kwen - khos'.   Si - ya - ham - ba,   ham - ba,   si - ya -
light   of   God.   We   are march-ing,   march-ing,   we   are
luz   de   Dios.   Ca - mi - nan - do   va - mos,   ca - mi -

G   Ooo   D7   ┌──3── ┐   G

ham - ba,   ham - ba si - ya - hamb' e - ku - kha - nyen' kwen - khos'.
march-ing,   march-ing, we are march-ing in   the   light   of   God.
nan - do,   va - mos, ca - mi - nan - do en   la   luz   de   Dios.

└──3──┘

294 Go to the World!

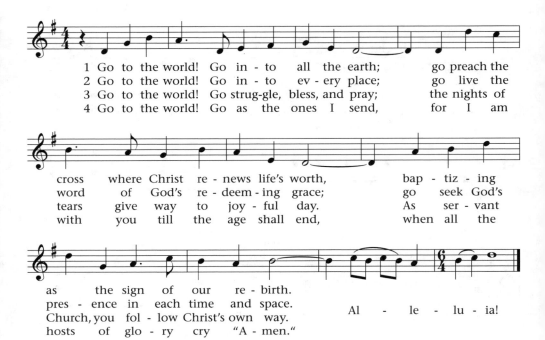

1 Go to the world! Go in-to all the earth; go preach the
2 Go to the world! Go in-to ev-ery place; go live the
3 Go to the world! Go strug-gle, bless, and pray; the nights of
4 Go to the world! Go as the ones I send, for I am

cross where Christ re-news life's worth, bap-tiz-ing
word of God's re-deem-ing grace; go seek God's
tears give way to joy-ful day. As ser-vant
with you till the age shall end, when all the

as the sign of our re-birth.
pres-ence in each time and space.
Church, you fol-low Christ's own way. Al - le - lu - ia!
hosts of glo-ry cry "A-men."

Text: Sylvia Dunstan (1955-1993)
Music: Charles Villiers Stanford (1852-1924)
Text © 1991, GIA Publications, Inc.

10 10 10 with alleluia
ENGELBERG

Acknowledgments and Index of Copyright Holders/Administrators

We are grateful to all individuals and publishers who have granted us permission to print their copyrighted materials. Every effort has been made to determine the owners and administrators of each copyright and to secure needed permission. We will be grateful to have any errors brought to our attention and will then make the necessary corrections in subsequent printings.

Permission to reproduce any copyrighted words or music contained in *Sing! A New Creation* must be obtained from the copyright holders of that material. For addresses of copyright holders not listed below, please contact CRC Publications.

All Scripture quotations are from the HOLY BIBLE, NEW REVISED STANDARD VERSION, © 1989 by the Division of Christian Education of National Council of the Churches of Christ in the USA. Used by permission. All rights reserved.

Permission has been granted by the copyright holders for the sources of all these other spoken texts:

2   James F. White and Susan J. White, as found in the *Book of Common Worship.*

22   Hughes Oliphant Old, based on Ephesians 1:3; adapted from *Leading in Prayer,* © 1995, Wm. B. Eerdmans Publishing Co.

46   John Paarlberg, adapted from *Reformed Worship* 35 (March, 1995), pp. 35-36. © 1995, CRC Publications.

52   From the *Book of Common Worship* (1946, 1993), Westminster/John Knox Press.

53   From the *Book of Worship,* © 1986, United Church of Christ Office for Church Life and Leadership.

55   John Paarlberg, as found in *Reformed Worship* 34 (December, 1994), p. 6. © 1994, CRC Publications.

76   (1) From *Worship the Lord,* © 1987, Wm. B. Eerdmans Publishing Co.; (2) From the *Book of Worship,* © 1986, United Church of Christ Office for Church Life and Leadership.

82   From *Worship the Lord,* Commission on Worship, Reformed Church in America.

94   John Paarlberg, © 2000.

99   From *Common Order,* © Panel on Worship of the Church of Scotland.

119 From *The Alternative Service Book 1980,* © 1980, The Central Board of Finance of the Church of England.

159 From *The Worshipbook: Services,* © 1970, The Westminster Press.

170 John Paarlberg, as found in *Reformed Worship* 55 (March, 2000), © 2000 CRC Publications.

176 As translated in 1989 for the Reformed Church in America.

194 John Paarlberg, © 2001.

217 From *Common Order,* © Panel on Worship of the Church of Scotland.

231 John Paarlberg, © 2001.

240 Adapted by John Paarlberg from the liturgy for the sacrament of baptism of the Reformed Church in America, 2001.

250 From the Liturgy of the Reformed Church in America, 1987.

283 From *Our World Belongs to God* as found in the *Psalter Hymnal,* © 1987, CRC Publications.

Augsburg Fortress
426 South Fifth Street
Minneapolis MN 55440
800-328-4648
Fax: 612-330-3455

BMG Music
1400 18th Ave S
Nashville TN 37212
615-858-1332
Fax: 615-858-1330

Brentwood-Benson Music
  Publishing, Inc.
741 Cool Springs
Franklin TN 37067
800-846-7664
Fax: 615-261-3386

Brier Patch Music
4324 Canal Avenue SW
Grandville MI 49418
616-534-6571
Fax: 616-534-1113

Brummhart Publishing
708 Blooming Grove Dr.
Rensselaer NY 12144-9420
518-286-1837

CRC Publications
(Faith Alive Christian Resources)
2850 Kalamazoo Ave. SE
Grand Rapids MI 49560
616-224-0785
Fax: 616-224-0834

Celebration
P.O. Box 309
Aliquippa PA 15001
724-375-1510
Fax: 724-375-1138

Celebremos/Libros Alianza
A. A. 100
Cucuta
COLOMBIA
57 7-574-2959
Fax: 57 7-574-4328

Changing Church, Inc.
200 East Nicollet Boulevard
Burnsville MN 55337
952-435-8102

Chinese Christian Literature Council
Flat A 4/F St Andrew's Christian
Centre, 138 Nathan Road
Kowloon, Hong Kong
CHINA
852-2367-8031-3
Fax: 852-2739-6030

Choristers Guild
2834 W. Kingsley Road
Garland TX 75041
972-271-1521
Fax: 972-840-3113

Christian Conference of Asia
Attn: Rev. Toshitsugu Arai
Pak Tin Village, Mei Tin Road
Shatin N T Hong Kong
CHINA

Panel on Worship
The Church of Scotland
121 George Street
Edinburgh EH2 4YN
SCOTLAND
0131-225-5722
Fax: 0131-220-3113

Concordia Publishing House
3558 Jefferson Avenue
St. Louis MO 63118
800-325-0191
Fax: 314-268-1329

Copyright Management Services, Inc.
1625 Broadway - 4th Floor
Nashville TN 37203
615-250-4600
Fax: 615-250-4699

Covenant Publications
5101 N. Francisco Avenue
Chicago IL 60625
773-784-3000
Fax: 773-784-4366

Earl Pleasant Publishing
PO Box 3247
Thond Oaks CA 91359
818-991-3728
Fax: 818-991-2567

earthsongs
220 NW 29th Street
Corvallis OR 97330
541-758-5760
Fax: 541-754-5887

Editorial Avance Luterano
2053 Woodland Heights Glen
Escondido CA 92026
760-736-0018
Fax: 760-736-0019

EMI Christian Music Publishing
PO Box 5085
101 Winners Circle
Brentwood TN 37024-5085
615-371-6880
Fax: 615-371-6897

Fricon Entertainment Co.
11 Music Square East, Suite 301
Nashville TN 37203
615-826-2288
Fax: 615-826-0500

GIA Publications, Inc.
7404 South Mason Avenue
Chicago IL 60638
800-442-1358
Fax: 708-496-3828

General Board of Global Ministries
United Methodist Church
475 Riverside Drive
New York NY 10115
Fax: 212-870-3748

Hope Publishing Company
380 South Main Place
Carol Stream IL 60188
800-323-1049
Fax: 708-665-2552

Integrity Music, Inc.
1000 Cody Road
Mobile AL 36695
334-633-9000
Fax: 334-633-9998

International Committee on English
  in the Liturgy, Inc.
1522 K Street NW, Suite 1000
Washington DC 20005
202-347-0800
Fax: 202-347-1839

Kevin Mayhew Ltd.
Buxhall Stowmarket
Suffolk IP14 3BW
ENGLAND
011-44-973-7978
Fax: 011-44-973-7834

Lilly Mack Music
421 E. Beach
Inglewood CA 90302
310-677-5603
Fax: 310-677-0250

Lorenz Publishing Co.
501 East 3rd Street
PO Box 802
Dayton OH 45401-0802
937-228-6118
Fax: 937-223-2042

Lumko Institute
PO Box 5058
Delmenville 1403
SOUTH AFRICA

Manna Music, Inc.
35255 Brooten Road
Pacific City OR 97135
503-965-6112
Fax: 503-965-6880

MorningStar Music Publishers
1727 Larkin Williams Rd.
Fenton MO 63026
636-305-0100
Fax: 636-305-0121

Music Sales
257 Park Avenue South
New York NY 10010
212-254-2100
Fax: 212-254-2013

Music Services
209 Chapelwood Drive
Franklin TN 37069
615-794-9015
Fax: 615-794-0793

OCP Publications
5536 NE Hassalo
Portland OR 97213
800-547-8992
Fax: 503-282-3486

Oxford University Press, Inc.
198 Madison Avenue
New York NY 10016-4314
212-726-6000
Fax: 212-726-6444

Pilgrim Press
700 Prospect Avenue, East
Cleveland OH 44115-1110
216-736-3764
Fax: 216-736-2207

Presbyterian Church in Canada
50 Wynford Drive
North York ON M3C 1J7
CANADA
416-441-1111
Fax: 416-441-2825

Puqi Jiang / Asian School of Music
Worship and the Arts
PO Box 10533 Broadway Centrum
Quezon City 1112
PHILIPPINES

Reformed Church in America
Commission on Worship
475 Riverside Drive
New York NY 10115
212-870-3020
Fax: 212-870-2499

Resource Publications
160 East Virginia St., Suite 290
San Jose CA 95112
408-286-8505
Fax: 408-287-8748

Selah Publishing
57 Pearl Street
PO Box 3037
Kingston NY 12401-0902
800-852-6172
Fax: 845-338-2991

Sovereign Lifestyle Music
PO Box 356
Leighton Buzzard UK LU7 3WP
44-1-525-385578
Fax: 44-1-525-372743

The Copyright Company
40 Music Square East
Nashville TN 37302
615-244-5588
Fax: 615-244-5591

The Royal School of Church Music
Cleveland Lodge, Westhumble
Dorking Surrey RH5 6BW
UK
011-44-130-687-7676
Fax: 011-44-130-688-7260
cl@rscm.com
www.rscm.com

The United Church Publishing House
3250 Bloor St. West, Suite 300
Etobicoke ON M8X 2Y4
CANADA
416-231-5931
Fax: 416-231-3103

United Church of Christ in Japan
2-3-18 Nishiwaseda
Shinjuku-ku Tokyo 169-0051
JAPAN
03-3294-0425
Fax: 03-3204-0457

Walton Music Corp.
PO Box 167
Bynum NC 27228
954-542-5548
Fax: 954-542-5527

Warner Brothers Publications, Inc.
15800 NW 48th Avenue
PO Box 4340
Miami FL 33014
305-521-1600
Fax: 305-625-3480

Wayne Leupold Editions
8510 Triad Drive
Colfax NC 27235
800-765-3196
Fax: 336-996-8445

Westminster/John Knox Press
100 Witherspoon Street
Louisville KY 40202-1396
502-569-5060
Fax: 502-569-5113

Wiseman Music
PO Box 7494
Bellevue WA 98008
425-401-8844
Fax: 425-644-8160

Wm. B. Eerdmans Publishing Co.
255 Jefferson Avenue SE
Grand Rapids MI 49503
616-459-4591
Fax: 616-459-6540

Word Music
3319 West End Ave. Suite 200
Nashville TN 37203
615-385-9673
Fax: 615-269-3190

World Council of Churches
150 route de Ferney
Geneva 2
SWITZERLAND
Fax: 011-41-22-791-0361

Metrical Index of Tunes

Index of Tune Names

Note: Several hymn tunes appear in abbreviated form as psalm refrains. Numbers for those shortened tunes are listed in italics.

Index of Authors, Composers, and Sources

Index of First Lines and Common Titles

Note: All spoken items are listed in italics.